GREAT EVENTS
IN THE LIFE OF
JOHN PAUL JONES

5 *Escapes from the West Indies after a mutiny aboard his own ship* Betsy, *1773*

6 *Appointed senior lieutenant of the new American navy flagship* Alfred, *1775*

8 *Wins lasting fame when his ship* Bonhomme Richard *wins the battle with the British frigate* Serapis, *1779*

7 *Raids British coal ships, aboard the* Ranger, *1778*

THE STORY OF
John Paul Jones

He had not far to walk before he saw the name

THE STORY OF
John Paul Jones

By IRIS VINTON

Illustrated by EDWARD A. WILSON

ENID LAMONTE MEADOWCROFT
Supervising Editor

PUBLISHERS Grosset & Dunlap NEW YORK

COPYRIGHT, 1953, BY IRIS VINTON

The Story of John Paul Jones

PRINTED IN THE UNITED STATES OF AMERICA

Library of Congress Catalog Card No. 52–13748

To
My Forebears from Galloway

Contents

Illustrations

ILLUSTRATIONS

THE STORY OF
John Paul Jones

"Wheesht!" warned the commander. "You're stirring up a storm!"

CHAPTER ONE

The Merchant Ship

THE five boys sat on their heels at the edge of the pool. A sixth boy stood on a rock hurling down commands at the fleet of little ships.

"Helm a-weather! Drop the peak! Square the main yard!" he shouted.

A puff of wind caught the sails. The toy ships sped across the quiet inlet on Scotland's seacoast. Two ran together and keeled over in a tangle of stick masts and bits of cloth.

"Abandon ship, you lubbers!" yelled the boy on the rock. "Your brigs are sinking like gallipots!"

The ships' owners were already wading after the wrecks. Their splashing churned up the shallow water.

"Wheesht!" warned the commander. "You're stirring up a storm."

[3]

The rest of the fleet tossed and rocked. Then some of the vessels capsized. Others ran aground among the pebbles and seashells. The three boys on shore ran to save their own ships.

"Johnnie!" they cried to the boy on the rock. "You best come down. Your own frigate's flopped on her side."

Johnnie started down, slithering over the seaweed that covered the clutter of rocks.

"Rorie! Wat! Rob! Tam! Andy!" he scolded as he scrambled. "Will you never learn, you loons? You wreck the fleet every time with your splashing!"

He bent over and picked up his frigate from the sand. Sails and rigging were all in place.

"No harm done," he announced, relieved.

But Tam's two ships and several of the others had not fared so well.

"We'll have to put into port for repairs," Rob stated solemnly.

Rorie, the redhead, examined his toy boat. Then he tossed it among the rocks. "I need a new ship entirely. Wat stomped on mine again," he accused the lean, ungainly boy next to him.

"I did not," denied Wat.

[4]

"You did! I ought to . . ." Rorie showed Wat his fist.

Johnnie stepped in between the two bigger boys. "There'll be no quarreling among the officers of His Majesty's Navy," he said sternly. "You'll all come aboard the flagship for a council."

With his ship under his arm, Johnnie detoured around the rocks and began to climb the bank.

The five hesitated. They were all about the same age as Johnnie. But they were all bigger than the ten-year-old. For a moment they considered disobeying orders. Johnnie was getting altogether too free with his "do this" and "do that."

Johnnie glanced over his shoulder. His friends stood in a quiet group.

He said briskly, "Lively there, Captain Rorie. We must repair the damage, or King George will learn that his fleet was wrecked by your carelessness."

"Aw, come off it, Johnnie Paul," Rorie said.

"Indeed, you're forgetting you're only the gardener's son," Andy laughed. He had a way of laughing spitefully that drew up his brown face like the drawstrings on a leather pouch.

"Well there's something you'd better not be forgetting either, Andy Pucker Face," Johnnie said calmly. "My father is the gardener for Mr. Craik, the Laird of Arbigland, on the Galloway coast of Scotland. And we do not sleep with the cow and pigs like some people I know."

Johnnie's tongue could be sharp. Andy often bragged that his family owned their own farm. But the truth was that Andy's family were as poor as the mice in Kirkbean kirk. And in winter the cow and three pigs occupied a shed next the big kitchen, which was the only room in their cottage.

Now Andy said nothing, for Johnnie had hurt his pride. Johnnie had a magic power over words—he could hurt people with a few words, or comfort them, or excite them.

It came, the boys believed, from reading and remembering enough to burst any other boy's head. He could work his word-magic to save their hides when they were caught in the laird's orchards. Or to sting them into doing what he wanted done.

Johnnie's black eyes flicked over Andy and

the others. He turned to face them and pushed his broad blue Scottish bonnet up from his forehead.

"I'll have you know," he roared, "as long as I'm commander here, you'll obey my orders. Or," he thundered, "you'll hang in chains in London Town in England by order of the King!"

He turned his back on them again and continued up the bankside.

Rorie chuckled, excited by Johnnie's bold words. "Did you ever hear the like?" he asked the group. Then, springing after Johnnie, he said, "Come on, lads. Step lively there."

The boys gathered up their broken ships and trailed after. They could always depend upon Johnnie to change the dull day to an exciting one. His skill in finding adventure kept them following where he led. He stood now at the top of the bank, gazing at the Solway Firth, which was a strip of sea between Scotland and England. Rorie, Rob, and the rest joined him.

The August day was clear. They shaded their eyes with their hands against the afternoon sun. Far down the Solway, they could see a ship. She was larger than the vessels that plied between the ports along the coast.

"She's from Virginia in the American colonies," Johnnie decided after a bit.

"How can you tell?" asked Tam. "She might be coming from London for all you know."

"Na, na." Johnnie shook his head. "Look at that cloud of sails. She's cutting the water for sure. Trading ships from the American colonies always travel as if Meg o' the Moss chased them on her broomstick."

"Ay," Rorie agreed. "She rides low in the water, too."

"If she's from Virginia," Andy said, "she'll have a hold full of tobacco and wheat most likely."

"If she's from Virginia," Johnnie repeated excitedly, "my brother Will may be aboard. Or he's sent a letter. Come on, we can see from the cliffs what port she's heading for."

They all set off at a jog trot on a narrow winding road along the bank. In a few minutes, the six boys went sliding down the slope to the shore. The wet white sand was easier on their bare feet than the rough road and they sped faster. Soon they came to the clean hard

[*8*]

beach where the cliffs rose in high arches and caverns on their right.

On the rocky walls men with baskets were perched on ledges or in rope swings. They were gathering samphire. The juicy parsley-like plant was much prized for pickles and sauces.

"Are you come to see the gallant merchant ship?" one of the pickers called to the boys.

"That we are," replied Johnnie.

"Then hurry up, so you can see her round the point," the men told them. "She's a great bonnie lass."

The boys picked their way over the rocks and began to climb. Soon they were standing on high jutting rocks. These were perfect places from which to watch ships in the Solway.

This one came bounding toward them with the wind at her back. She swooped around the point. She glided over the water swift as a falcon. Her high masts and square sails seemed to scrape the blue sky.

"Aye, she's bonnie, bonnie," Johnnie breathed. Just watching the beauty made a lump come into his throat. The vessel was new and fine and he had never seen her before in

[9]

*Her high masts and square sails seemed
to scrape the blue sky*

the Solway. As she moved closer, the boys could see the water curling in white foam off her bow.

"Watch her go!" exclaimed a samphire picker. "She's got to make it over the sandbar before low tide."

In another moment, the ship had passed them. Then, keeping to the deep water, she began to come about.

Johnnie clutched Rorie's shoulder. "The ship's making for the mouth of the river!" he cried. "She's bound for Carsethorn! We'll go aboard. And if my brother Will . . ."

Johnnie started down the cliff. As soon as his feet touched the sand, he began to run.

"Hey, Johnnie!" Rorie called after him. "Bide a wee. Don't you see it's most sundown? We have to get home to do our chores."

"I know," answered Johnnie. Without breaking stride, he added, "But my father will take me to Carsethorn in the cart."

The five boys clambered down. In a straggling band, they trotted along the gleaming beach behind Johnnie Paul.

CHAPTER TWO

Letter from Will

A T THE three crossroads, Johnnie and the boys separated. They all ached to go to Carsethorn. But failure to be home before sundown meant feeling the smart of the birch switch.

Johnnie ran on alone toward Arbigland, which was the name of the laird's big farm near the mouth of the Nith River. The long summer day was almost ended when the gardener's stone cottage came in sight.

He heard clucking and gobbling and a pan being banged with a stone. Mary Ann, his eight-year-old sister, was getting the chickens and turkeys together to be fed.

The cottage sat facing the road. At one side a weathered fence enclosed the cottage garden. When he reached the fence corner, he stopped and climbed up. Balancing himself on the top

Balancing on the top rail, he looked across the Solway

rail, he looked across the Solway and then up the Nith River. But the merchant ship was gone. The tree-covered ridge hid Carsethorn. So he could not tell if the vessel was anchored in the bay.

He got down and hurried toward the barn. He hoped his father had come home from work.

His two older sisters, Elizabeth and Janet, were in the barn, milking. The girls' caps were snowy patches against the black flanks of the cows.

Maggy, the Galloway pony, greeted him with a friendly nicker. Sandy, the ancient collie, came from under the cart to lick his hand.

"Where's Father?" Johnnie asked from the barn doorway.

"Weel, it's about time you came," said Elizabeth.

"Did you swim the Solway from Scotland to England?" asked Janet jokingly. "You've been gone the whole day."

"Rorie and I swam a lot this morning," Johnnie replied. "But then the others came. They're afraid to learn to swim, the ninnies. They'll make sorry sailors."

Elizabeth gave a loud sniff. " 'Tis little you know of sailors, Johnnie Paul," she told him. "They do not hold with swimming. When your ship goes down, it's best to drown at once."

Elizabeth and Janet were so much older than he was that Johnnie often thought he had three mothers instead of one.

"Please quit talking and tell me where Father is," Johnnie pleaded.

"He's gone to Carsethorn with Mr. Craik," replied Elizabeth.

"Carsethorn!" Johnnie exclaimed. "But why did they go to Carsethorn without me?"

"They couldn't very well take you if you weren't here, could they?" Janet asked patiently. "They looked for you after the messenger came with news for the laird."

Disappointment touched off Johnnie's quick temper. Stamping his foot, he shouted, "What news? Why wasn't there any news for *us?*"

"Now don't you fly up in the snuff at me, my lad," eighteen-year-old Elizabeth told him. "You'll get nothing from me acting that way."

"A special messenger came from the Custom House at Kirkcudbright," explained six-teen-year-old Janet. "To tell Mr. Craik he had goods on board a ship. The goods were from his son James, the doctor, in Virginia. And Mr. Craik was to go fetch them when the ship arrived in Carsethorn."

"But why wasn't there any letter from brother Will?" Johnnie cried.

"The messenger came from the Custom House," snapped Elizabeth. "If there's a let-ter, Father will get it from the captain of the ship."

Johnnie turned and walked, dragging his feet, across the barnyard. He saw Mary Ann flirting her apron at the turkey cock to drive him away from the kitchen door. He looked at his little sister with approval. She was such a tidy, prim little person.

"Johnnie!" she cried. "Father and Mr. Craik were looking for you."

"I know," he said.

"I had to get the peat for the fire," she went on. "But you better hurry and fetch water from the well. Or Mother will be ready to take you in hand."

"I'm sorry about the peat, my bonnie," her

brother apologized. He took down a yoke from the side of the house. He hung two wooden buckets at either end and lifted the yoke across his slender shoulders. He made two trips to the well, while he thought about the ship and the possible letter from Will.

When he had finished, he gathered a basket of dry chips and went into the kitchen. His mother was bent over the griddle, making oatcakes. How good they smelled! Johnnie thought that in another minute his stomach would collapse from hunger.

[17]

He set the basket of chips on the hearth. "Are we going to wait supper for Father?" he asked his mother.

"Oh, it's you, Johnnie, at last." She peered round at him. "Na, na. I want to get supper out of the way. The chickens for Sabbath dinner have to be roasted yet. Your father will sup when he comes. Take the wood spoon, and stir the porridge."

That was right. He had almost forgot. To-day was Saturday. Tomorrow was the Sabbath. And all work stopped as though Time cast a spell upon it.

His mother always prepared Sunday dinner on Saturday. Then the Sabbath was free for going to kirk and reading the Good Book.

"Mother, do you think the ship will leave tomorrow?" he asked worriedly.

"Now, Johnnie, lad," advised Mrs. Paul, "don't you fret about that ship. It won't move until after Monday market." Monday was the day all the farmers went to sell their butter, eggs, and vegetables at Carsethorn market.

A warm glow filled Johnnie. He might get to go aboard the ship after all. He stirred the porridge vigorously.

The two girls came in with the milk. Mary Ann brought the bowls and horn spoons. Mrs. Paul ladled out the porridge and Johnnie carried the bowls to the table. Elizabeth brought the hot oatcakes and butter and Janet, the pitcher of milk.

Johnnie could scarcely wait until his mother said grace to tuck into his bowl. He heard Sandy bark joyfully and a voice say, "Waiting for me, were you? There's a good dog."

"That's Father!" Johnnie cried, jumping up.

"Sit you right down again," ordered his mother. "You'll not be popping up and down in the middle of your meal."

He sank to the bench.

"Ay, Mother, I'm sorry to be late," Mr. Paul apologized to his wife as he came in. "But the laird and I had to unpack the American fox-grape vines."

"Mary Ann," said Mrs. Paul quickly. "Fill a bowl for your father." She turned back to her husband. "I know you're bringing a letter from Will. Otherwise you and the laird would be *planting* the grapevines this night."

[*19*]

"Ay," said Mr. Paul, sitting down at the head of the table. "A long letter."

From inside his blue bonnet, Mr. Paul removed a folded sheet of paper. Mary Ann set a bowl of porridge and a cup of hot tea in front of him. Between spoonfuls of porridge and sips of tea, he read the letter.

"Dear Mother and Father, Sisters, and Brother Johnnie," William Paul had written. "It has been a long time since you've heard from me. Almost a year, I think. But, as you know, I was sailmaker on a vessel voyaging in outlandish places. There was no way of sending letters.

"But now, bless God, I'm back in Virginia. I am setting up a tailor shop in the thriving town of Fredericksburg. The prospect is all that I could wish. My only regret is that I could not visit you before I settled here . . ."

There was a great deal more about the plantations and fine trade. And about the many chances poor men had for bettering themselves in America. But Johnnie listened with only half an ear. Will wasn't coming home. That was the important thing. Will was going to become a great man with land and a shop of his own—a laird, no less, in far-off Virginia.

The letter was finished and supper was done with. A sigh went round the table.

"Though it's a far distance from home," said Mr. Paul, "I'd not wish him back. William will be rich and happy in the new land."

Mrs. Paul's dark eyes were thoughtful. "It's true," she agreed. "He'd never do so well here at home. Never."

Her manner became brisk. "Johnnie, go poke up the fire and hang a rushlight on the wall. I want to wash the dishes and start the fowls roasting on the spit."

Johnnie hopped up. As he lit the wick of the rushlight, he wished he were on the ocean sailing to Virginia. And that made him think again of the merchant ship in Carsethorn.

"Father, we're going to Monday market, aren't we?" he asked.

Mr. Paul glanced up into his son's eager black eyes. "We are," he said. "The laird has some cargo to put on board the ship, so I'll be needing a helper."

Johnnie grinned. He felt like crowing as his thoughts skipped ahead to Monday and the ship at Carsethorn.

[*21*]

CHAPTER THREE

Monday Market

JOHNNIE woke with a start. At first he could not think what had wakened him. Then he heard the loud gobble of a turkey outside the window.

"It was the bubbly-jock waked me," he decided.

Johnnie sat up and swung his feet to the floor. Today was Monday, he thought joyfully. He stood up. Taking his shirt and breeches off the peg on the wall, he began to dress.

Soon finished, he grasped a rung of the ladder and dropped lightly to the floor below. His bare feet padded across the kitchen flagstones.

Quickly he gathered up some peat from the stack by the door. He staggered inside with a load. He stirred up the coals. He put on some chips, and got the fire going.

Then he went to help his father clean the barn. His father watched him furiously pitching manure out the barn door.

Then he asked, "Johnnie, my joe, where's the fire in the heather? We must wait on the women and I must fetch the laird from the mansion house before we can go to market."

At seven o'clock, when Johnnie was about ready to burst with the delay, his father came back from the mansion house. He was driving the big farm wagon, loaded with bales of sheepskins for the upriver tanneries at Dumfries. And beside Mr. Paul on the wagon seat was Mr. Craik, the laird.

The laird was a grave, kindly man who wore his Scottish bonnet proudly. He did not hold with the new fashion of wearing hats.

"Loup up, lad," Mr. Craik told Johnnie as the team and wagon stopped before the door. "Where are your mother and your sisters?"

Before Johnnie could answer, Maggy, the Galloway pony, came round the corner of the house, pulling the red cart. In it were Mrs. Paul, the girls, baskets of eggs, crocks of butter, and jars of samphire pickles.

They exchanged good mornings with the

[23]

"Loup up, lad," Mr. Craik told Johnnie

laird. Mr. Paul clucked to the horses. Elizabeth slapped Maggy's reins. And they all set out on the road through the dark wood, then up the tree-covered ridges.

They passed the village of Kirkbean. Then in a few minutes they were in Carsethorn. Its whitewashed cottages hugged the sea front. In the yards cabbages and bright flowers jostled each other in happy confusion.

But this confusion was as nothing compared with that at the market. Fishwives had gathered at the market place with creels of fresh flounder and salmon. Farm wives had baskets of eggs and pats of butter to sell.

Sheep, chickens, and turkeys were all raising their voices above the lilting Scottish speech and the strange-sounding English of the American sailors.

The cart with Johnnie's mother and sisters stopped at the market place. The farm wagon with Johnnie and the two men rolled on slowly toward the waterfront.

Johnnie looked anxiously to the right and left. Finally, he saw Rorie and Wat and Andy standing before two sailors. The boys were all talking at once, flapping their arms excitedly.

The sailors were laughing and nudging each other.

"Hullo!" cried Johnnie. "We're going to the big ship!"

The three boys turned, ran to the wagon, and hopped up in the back.

"The sailors told us we couldn't get on the ship," Rorie, the redhead, said. "They say there's a fierce American beast running loose on deck."

"I don't believe it," Wat said flatly. "It's a lie."

Just then they came to the end of the street and looked out on the harbor. The merchant ship lay some way out. But the ship's longboat was drawn up on the beach, with several sailors waiting to take the laird's cargo aboard.

With the help of the boys, the sailors soon had the goods stowed in the boat. At a nod from the Laird of Arbigland, Johnnie and his friends leaped in too.

Mr. Craik settled himself at the bow. Then as the sailors shoved off, he said, "Will you not change your mind, Mr. Paul, and go along?"

"Na, na," replied Johnnie's father from the wagon seat. "I've no great liking for ships."

The sailors bent to their oars and the boat moved over the water. When they bumped alongside the ship, Johnnie gazed up the ladder which hung over the side. It seemed to reach up as high as the Solway cliffs.

"Good morning to you, Captain," the laird called up to the man in the tricorn hat, leaning over the ship's side.

"Morning, Mr. Craik," replied the captain. "Up the ladder, boy," he ordered Johnnie, who stood on a pile of skins.

To a boy used to climbing about rocks and crags, going up the ladder was nothing. Johnnie was swinging his leg over the side to the deck above in a moment.

"You're pretty young for an old salt," the American captain praised him. "But you mounted the ladder natural as breathing."

Rorie, then Andy and Wat clambered over the side.

The captain roared, "Josiah! Josiah! Come here, you rascal!"

A rangy, freckled-faced lad of about twelve or thirteen came tearing up and saluted.

"Josiah, show these young Scotsmen over the ship," the captain ordered.

[27]

"Up the ladder, boy," the captain ordered Johnnie

"Aye, aye, sir," replied Josiah, saluting again smartly. He made a motion for the boys to follow him. He led them to the bow where they clustered around him. They eyed him from the bright handkerchief tied about his head to the stout black shoes on his feet.

He returned their curious glances calmly. He observed the Scottish bonnets with the red bobs on top, the patched breeches, the short sturdy jackets.

"Where's your home?" Johnnie asked.

"Boston," replied the boy.

"Then you're an American," Johnnie said quickly. "That's in the colonies."

"That's right. We're all Americans from the captain down to me. I'm the cabin boy. Ship's American, too. Built in Boston. And she's the sweetest sailer afloat." He reeled it all off proudly. Then added, "What else you want to know?"

Johnnie ignored the question. "Weel, she's not so bad for one of our colonial merchant ships," he said.

"What do you mean—not so bad?" demanded Josiah, glaring at the smaller Scots boy. "I'll lay two fingers on a chopping block if you've seen any ships that are cleaner."

Johnnie looked around the deck. Everything on it was in place. He studied the white furled sails and stout rigging.

"Aweel, she seems well regulated," he said slowly. "But no doubt she's an exception to the general rule." Then he asked, as though it didn't really matter, "What about the wild beast?"

"Ay," Wat spoke up at once, "two of your sailors spoke of it. They said it wears a black mask and washes its victim before it eats it."

The glint of anger in Josiah's gray eyes was replaced by a merry twinkle. He drew himself up. From his full height he towered over the boys.

"I'd rather not talk about the animal, if you don't mind," he said with dignity. "The captain owns an interest himself in this vessel. So he can bring on board whatever he likes. But we've had some terrible times . . ." He let his voice trail off sadly.

Johnnie's nose twitched. He liked the cabin boy with his frank open face. But he wouldn't put it past him to have a trick buried near by. Johnnie smelled it.

[30]

Josiah said briskly, "Let me show you the ship."

He led them up ladders and down. Through seamen's quarters to the captain's cabin. They tried steering and marching around the capstan. Through it all, one boy or another would ask about the wild animal, but not a word could they get out of Josiah.

By the time they got to the galley entrance, they had decided the thing was a joke. The captain and Mr. Craik, walking down the passage below deck, saw them standing near the galley.

"Josiah, give the boys some peanuts," said the captain. "Then they're to be ready to go ashore with Mr. Craik."

"Aye, aye, sir," answered Josiah. He pushed the boys before him into the galley. Then he went into the storeroom beyond and brought out a big bowl of what he called peanuts.

"Have some," he invited. "They come from Virginia. Don't scatter the shells."

The boys cracked them between their fingers. The nuts were delicious. It was odd they grew on vines in the ground as Josiah said.

While they were waiting, Josiah asked in an

[*31*]

offhand way, "Would you like to see the animal?"

Johnnie looked around quickly. He thought he had heard Josiah chuckle. The next moment, Josiah came out of the storeroom. In his arms he carried a small gray animal with a bright pointed face and forepaws like tiny black hands.

"I thought I'd find you in there eating honey," he scolded. "Cookie will wallop you."

The boys gazed at the animal in amazement, then burst into laughter.

"So that's the wild beast!" they cried.

"I thought there was a trick somewhere," Johnnie said. "What is it?"

"It's the captain's pet raccoon. His name's Scrub. Here, I'll show you why," the cabin boy said.

Josiah put a cup of water on the table. He got a biscuit, gave it to the raccoon and set the pet on the table. At once, the animal dipped the biscuit into the water and began to wash it.

The boys watched delightedly.

"Can I pick him up?" Johnnie asked.

"Sure, pick him up," Josiah said. "He won't bite if you're careful."

[32]

All the boys stretched out their arms toward the raccoon. Scrub was frightened. He leaped from the table. He fled like a flash down the passage, and up the ladder to the deck. The boys went tumbling after him.

The captain thrust his head out of his cabin door at the racket.

"Josiah!" he warned in a loud voice. "Catch that 'coon before he goes aloft. I don't want him up there when we set sail. He'll get hurt."

Johnnie crowded past the others and flew up the ladder. The raccoon raced down the deck and sprang up into the rigging. Johnnie was right behind him. They climbed the ropes and stays of the foremast. Then up the rat-lines. Scrub reached the foretop and walked out on the yardarm. He settled down. His bright look dared Johnnie to follow.

"Johnnie, come down, you'll break your neck," yelled Andy.

Johnnie paid no attention to Andy or the shouting far below on deck. He was not going to leave the wee thing up there to get hurt. He straddled the yardarm and pulled himself along with his hands.

"Scrub, you winsome thing, I'll not harm

[*33*]

you," he coaxed. He waited. Scrub didn't move. Gently, Johnnie reached out and drew the animal toward him. He cuddled it against his shoulder.

Then he looked around. He wondered if it would be easier going back the way he had come. Or sliding down that rope which ran from the yardarm to the deck. He had often slid down the tackle rope from the hayloft in the laird's big barn.

Someone started to shout as Johnnie wrapped his legs about the taut rope. Suddenly it became wonderfully quiet below. Johnny lowered himself slowly and grasped the rope with his right hand. He eased Scrub around to his back. Scrub clung to him as he would to a tree branch.

Johnnie grasped the rope with both his hands. Then he let himself go just as he did on the tackle rope that lifted the hay into the big, high barn.

Down they shot to the deck. Johnnie landed lightly on the balls of his feet. Josiah picked Scrub like a burr from Johnnie's back.

"Laddie, laddie, you had my heart in my mouth," said Mr. Craik. "But it does not hurt

Johnnie wrapped his legs about the taut rope

to say, now you're safe, it was a bonnie show of bravery."

"Young man," said the ship's captain, "I've half a notion to give you a berth right now. If ever I saw a born seaman, you're it! You take to ship's rigging like a duck to water."

Rorie, Wat, and Andy regarded their small friend with envy. Johnnie could feel his chest swell out with pride. He tried to keep it out of his tone as he spoke to the captain.

"Thank you, sir. But there's nothing much to sliding down a rope," he said.

The captain threw back his head and laughed hard. "Listen to the sprout!" he exclaimed. "Why, I've able seamen who'd not dare slide down the braces."

CHAPTER FOUR

The Jackdaw's Cage

IT WAS a dark, misty morning late in October. Johnnie held Mary Ann's hand tightly as they trudged the road to Kirkbean Parish school. Both their book satchels were slung across his back with a leather thong. Mary Ann held her shawl snug about her shoulders.

At the main road, Rob and Tam were waiting for them. They fell into step. They all went on side by side with their heads bent against the wind and misty rain.

After a little more than a mile, they came to the low hill at the edge of the village. Just around the curve at the top of the hill was the manse where school was kept.

The manse was the parson's house. For the Dominie, as all the people called him, was the

[*37*]

parson as well as the schoolmaster for Kirkbean Parish.

At the door of the manse, the boys wiped
their clogs and entered the hall. They heard
the buzz of voices behind the closed door at
their right.

"We're late!" Johnnie exclaimed at once.
He hated to be late for school. He burst into
the schoolroom like a small whirlwind.

It was a long, low room with a heavy, ink-
stained table, and some benches and book-
lined shelves. At the end near the fireplace was
a desk and a chair for the Dominie.

At once Johnnie saw that the schoolmaster
had not come downstairs. Rorie stood near the
Dominie's desk, surrounded by boys and girls.

[*38*]

Their heads were bent over something on the floor. Johnnie dropped the book satchels on the table and crowded up with the others.

In a homemade willow cage, Rorie had a jackdaw. The bird's glossy black feathers drooped. Its silvery gray head was buried in its breast.

Rorie had a stick and he was poking it between the bars to stir the bird up. "Wake up, you beggar!" he ordered, giving the bird a prod. "You were lively enough before. Now, talk."

The bird lifted its head and gave a tired croak.

"Let it alone, Rorie," said one of the girls. "You've hurt it."

"What do you think I caught it for, silly?" asked Rorie. "I'm going to teach it to talk. Jackdaws learn to talk better than parrots. Say good morning," he demanded, jabbing at the bird.

Aroused, the jackdaw squawked and beat the air helplessly with its wings.

Rorie laughed. "Well, that's better!" he exclaimed.

A sudden, crazy fury took hold of Johnnie

[39]

He thrust open the casement and let the jackdaw free

Paul. Elbowing his way to the front, he grabbed the birdcage.

"You'll not cage a poor, wild thing and torture it, Rorie of Maxwell!" he cried.

Before anyone knew what Johnnie was about, he had rushed with the cage to the window. There he thrust open the casement and let the jackdaw free. He watched the black-and-silver bird spread its wings and fly up into the oak tree. He tossed the cage out the window to the ground.

"I'll get you for this, Johnnie Paul," Rorie threatened in a low, ugly voice.

The threat was echoed by growls from the boys. The girls murmured and drew away, expecting a fight to start. Mary Ann screamed a warning, "Johnnie!"

Then, above the quick shuffle of boys' feet toward Johnnie, was heard the warm, kindly voice of the Dominie.

"Good morning to you, lads and lasses," he greeted them cheerfully.

The group swirled around. There in the doorway was the sandy-haired schoolmaster.

"And good morning to you, sir," they responded brightly.

[41]

Johnnie and the others could not guess how long the Dominie had stood in the doorway. But if he thought the boys were about to fight, he never let on.

For he said at once, "Let us sing the Psalm for today." And he recited the first line of the 121st Psalm, "I will lift up mine eyes unto the hills, from whence cometh my help."

He nodded. All fifteen of his pupils sang the Psalm heartily. After their "Amen" rang out, they scrambled for their places at the benches alongside the big table.

In the scramble, Rorie warned Johnnie, "You wait. I'll get even."

Johnnie pretended not to hear.

"Take out your copybooks. Look to your quills," said the Dominie.

The writing lesson began. Johnnie filled two pages with his clear, round handwriting.

He sat tickling his ear with the feather of his goosequill, with his eyes on Rorie. He knew that the big boy meant to catch him at eleven o'clock when they stopped for their "elevenses"—their midmorning lunch. Rorie would give him a licking, too, unless he could outwit him.

[42]

"I don't care," Johnnie thought. "I'm not sorry I let his bird loose. Tormenting it the way he did."

"Johnnie, have you nothing to do?" asked the Dominie.

Johnnie sat up quickly. "No, sir," he answered. "I'm finished, sir."

This did not surprise the Dominie. Johnnie usually finished his lessons before anyone else. The schoolmaster was always having to think of something more to keep Johnnie busy. Another arithmetic problem. Another page of Latin to put into English. The next chapter of a book. Some verses to learn by heart.

He studied his small, bright-faced pupil now. "Take your copybook, Johnnie," he said, "and go sit by the globe of the world. Write about a journey by ship to Bangkok."

Instantly, Johnnie was on his feet. "Yes, sir!" he exclaimed. It was just the kind of lesson he liked best of all.

Johnnie sat on the high stool by the big, round globe. The copybook was on his knee. The goosequill was behind his ear. The inkpot was within easy reach on the Dominie's desk.

[43]

"Now to find Bangkok," he thought, tracing a coastline on the map with a fingertip. "The China Sea. I must find the China Sea."

The schoolroom no longer existed for Johnnie. Rorie's threat was forgotten. Johnnie was off to the China Seas.

"Aren't you going for your elevenses?" asked the Dominie mildly, placing a hand on Johnnie's shoulder.

The boy looked around, startled. The schoolroom was empty except for the two of them.

"Oh, yes, sir," he replied. "I didn't know it was so late." He hopped down off the stool and began putting his things neatly in place on the table.

"Let me have your copybook," said the Dominie. "I'll read what you've written while I have my tea." He went over and poked up the peat fire. "I expect you know that Rorie and the other lads are waiting for you out front," he said, giving Johnnie a sharp glance over his shoulder.

"Yes, sir," answered Johnnie. "I thought they would be."

"Just so you know," said the Dominie. And putting the copybook under his arm, he left the room.

"Rorie's bigger than I am," Johnnie thought. "He can lick me in no time. But he was wrong. It's mean and cowardly to harm a creature when it can't help itself."

Johnnie worked himself up to a great pitch of fury as he stripped off his coat and his new stockings and his clogs. No matter what happened, he wasn't going to ruin his only coat and his new wool stockings.

He went to the window, opened it and swung outside, shutting it after him. He picked up Rorie's birdcage which was still lying on the ground.

He sailed around the corner of the manse and into the group of boys. They fell back in astonishment.

"Rorie!" shouted Johnnie. "Here's your birdcage. You're lower than a weasel. I'm ready to fight if you are. But you have to catch me first."

Turning on his heel, Johnnie made for the corner of the low manse roof. Clambering up, he crawled to the ridge of the roof.

He stood up and roared down at the boys, "Admit you're wrong, Rorie of Maxwell, to torment a poor, wild thing. You're a coward. You're afraid to take a dare!"

"Anything you dare to do I'll do!" declared Rorie, swinging onto the edge of the roof.

The other boys shouted with eager delight at what promised to be a great battle.

"Then slide down the chimney to the fire below," yelled Johnnie to Rorie. He raced

[46]

toward the tall chimney at the end of the house.

He hoisted himself up and sat on the edge, his feet hanging into the opening. The mist made a ghostly shadow of his small figure. The smoke from the fire in the schoolroom rolled up around him in stifling clouds. Ribbons of flame seemed to lick about him, though they really didn't. As he sat on the chimney edge, they only warmed his cold feet and legs.

But to the boys in the yard, it seemed that Johnnie was burning like a piece of pitch pine.

"Johnnie! Johnnie!" howled Andy. "You'll be roasted alive. Johnnie, don't!"

"Then Rorie has to admit he's wrong. Or I'll go down the chimney like a chimney

[47]

sweep," threatened Johnnie. "And Rorie's a coward and worse than a worm."

"But there's a fire down there!" screamed Tam.

"I know it," replied Johnnie. "Come on, Rorie. Here I go." He began to lower himself into the chimney.

"What in the name of all goodness goes on here?" demanded the Dominie, who came running out of the manse door.

"Johnnie's trying to roast himself to death on account of the jackdaw," explained Tam, yelling and whimpering at the same time.

"Johnnie! Johnnie Paul! Get down out of that chimney this instant! At once! Rorie, get off the roof. What are you lads doing up there anyway? I thought the manse was on fire." The Dominie was in a furious temper.

Meekly the two boys crawled down off the roof. They faced the Dominie with lowered heads.

"I never heard of anything so outrageous!" declared the Dominie. "Rorie, don't you ever bring a caged bird to the manse again. And Johnnie, you take care. You're heading straight for trouble, taking chances like that.

[48]

Now, shake hands, the two of you, and behave yourselves in the future."

Johnnie put out his hand and Rorie took it.

"We're even?" asked Johnnie.

"We're even," replied Rorie.

The girls came scampering from the kitchen and demanded to know what had happened.

"It was a brave show," the boys told them excitedly. "Johnnie started to climb down the chimney. And he dared Rorie to climb too. But the Dominie stopped them."

"That Johnnie Paul!" they all whooped gleefully.

"He's a knotty twig, he is! He's not feared of a thing in this world!" yelled Andy, slapping his leg.

CHAPTER FIVE

The Spyglass

FOR his eleventh birthday on July 6, 1758, the laird gave Johnnie an old brass spyglass.

"Now, you'll be able to spy out each ship that comes up the Solway," said Mr. Craik. "And you can see across to the wharves on the opposite shore."

The laird had a warm spot in his heart for this lad who played, worked, studied so fiercely.

Johnnie grasped the spyglass as though he were afraid it would get away. He thanked Mr. Craik many times. Then he swung himself up to the top of the garden wall by the apple trees. And he stood surveying the country round about. But most of all it was the sea he watched.

It was wonderful to have a spyglass. By day
he carried it in the pocket of his waistcoat, although it was heavy and weighed him down.
By night he kept it beside his bed together
with *Robinson Crusoe,* the book the Dominie
had ordered from London for him to read.

He was glad he had his spyglass and his book
that July.

That was a bad month for people on the
farms in Scotland. The crops were poor. Some
of the older boys left home to work in the tanneries at Dumfries upriver. Many of them, like
Rorie and Wat, got jobs aboard the boats. One
mouth less to feed meant much to their fam-
ilies.

Johnnie missed his schoolmates when it was
harvest time and the tenant farmers came to

give their labor for the laird's haying. He
helped to rake the hay as usual. At eleven in
the morning and four in the afternoon, he carried the tea from the mansion house to the
haymakers. Then for an hour or more in the
morning and again in the afternoon, he sat
alone on a haycock.

He drank his tea and trained his spyglass
upon the white sails of ships on the Solway and
the curls of smoke of the coast towns. He
longed to go to the places he had read about.
He wanted to be on a ship going some place.

"Your mother and I wish you would forget
about ships until you're older, Johnnie," Mr.

Paul often said. "You can learn to be a gardener and work for the laird."

"But you let Will go to sea," Johnnie pointed out. "And he was only a little older than I am. And look at him now."

There was no denying that William Paul had done well to leave home. He was becoming prosperous in America. His tailor shop in Fredericksburg was doing a fine business.

With the coming of winter, times grew still harder in Scotland. The Laird of Arbigland was a good master. But he had many people depending upon him. And much to drain his pockets of money. So it was to be expected that his gardener and his family would have to go without things which they needed. They skimped on food. And their clothes grew worn and shabby.

Now, when Johnnie talked of getting work as a ship's boy, his parents were not so quick to say he should not. They felt that in Galloway the son of a gardener had little chance of rising in the world. He would do well if he could keep from being hungry.

"Johnnie is vexed with a discontented spirit," Mrs. Paul told the Dominie at the table one bitter cold night. "When his nose is not buried in a book, he frets to be off at sea."

The Dominie had been caught in the snowstorm on his round of parish visits and had stopped at the Pauls'. He sat with the family over a supper of smoked fish and potatoes and samphire pickles.

"Mrs. Paul," said the Dominie, "Johnnie's spirit of discontent will always be with him. You might as well ask an eagle to change its nature and act like a wren."

"Ay, that's what I'm thinking," agreed Mr. Paul, glancing sideways at his son. "Johnnie wants to try his wings. And now that things are so hard at home, it's as good a time as any. What say you, Dominie?"

The parson smiled across the table at Johnnie. "I'm thinking I'd let him try," he said. "And I'll make up a package of books, so he'll not lack for reading."

"You'll get your wish, Johnnie," said his father. "Ships' captains stop often at the mansion house to stay the night. I'll ask the laird to speak to them about a job for you."

Joy and ache mingled in Johnnie's heart. It was joy to know he could be a sailor. It was ache to know he would have to leave home and family and friends.

But he said jauntily, "Tomorrow, I'll begin to ready my sea chest."

Many weeks passed. Johnnie's sea chest with a shirt, an extra pair of breeches and stockings, several books, and the spyglass, had been ready for a long time.

But December came and as yet no captain who visited the laird's mansion house had need of a boy on his ship.

Then came a snowy Saturday when Johnnie and Tam—one of his few remaining schoolmates—were playing on the ice down at the pond. Mr. Paul with the laird and a ship's captain came searching for them.

"Johnnie, lad, come here!" called Mr. Paul.

Johnnie ran to his father. He said, "Good day, sir," to the laird and looked curiously at the weather-beaten man in the thick sea jacket.

Mr. Craik said to the stranger, "Captain, this is the lad I was telling you of."

The captain looked Johnnie over carefully. "Mmm . . . I had in mind a bigger lad," he remarked. "But I'll take your word, Mr. Craik, that he's a good worker."

[55]

The captain looked Johnnie over carefully

"Johnnie can . . ." began Mr. Paul.

"Johnnie Paul will not disappoint you," interrupted the laird.

The captain spoke directly to Johnnie. "It's rough work on a collier," he said. "We carry coal from one town to the other. Dirty, hard work it is. You've not worked ship before. Do you think you can stand up to it without running home the first chance you get?"

"Yes, sir," answered Johnnie without hesitation. He returned the captain's searching gaze with quiet confidence.

"Then it's settled," said the captain. "You're hired, Johnnie, my lad. Get your gear and come aboard."

CHAPTER SIX

Johnnie Goes to Sea

THE captain was ready to sail that very day. As the collier lay at Carsethorn, they had not far to travel. Johnnie went home with his father for his sea chest. When he heard the laird's coach stop before the door, Johnnie hurried outside. Mary Ann flew after him and threw her arms about him.

"Johnnie, I don't want you to go," she cried. "You might never come back."

"Why, my wee bonnie, I'm not going on a ship across the sea," he consoled her. "Only on a collier that sails about our own Solway Firth. I'll be back in no time."

He gave her a quick kiss. Thrusting her away, he ran to the coach and handed up his sea chest to the driver. Then climbing up to the high seat, he waved to his family standing in the dooryard. The snow was hard-packed. The runners the laird had put on his coach made it go skimming over the road.

Within the hour, Johnnie Paul was on board the collier. He was told to help the cook and make himself generally useful. That afternoon they slipped out of Carsethorn on the tide and the vessel made its way out into the Solway.

The captain was a rough and ready man with a rough and ready crew. The collier was an old vessel and thoroughly blackened by years of carrying coal.

But from the first, Johnnie loved the plucky little craft. On the first night out, they ran into a gale. The collier rolled and tossed. The water poured over the deck. Yet she plowed steadily on through the foaming waves which rushed at her.

Johnnie spilled a great deal of porridge, tea, and salt-meat stew before he finally carried some safely from the galley to the captain's table. The cook gave him a week to get his sea legs.

"After that I'll take a strap to you, if you spill good food and costly tea," the cook promised him.

But altogether the skipper, the cook, and the men proved decent enough. So long as Johnnie did what he was told quickly, they took him for granted. He was one of the hands. They expected him to haul on the lines, take a place at the capstan, be a seaman like the rest.

Johnnie obeyed orders to the letter. Because he was new and willing and smart as paint, some of the crew took advantage of him. It was: "Johnnie, come here. Do this. Do that. Hoist the box. Dog-down-the-hatch. Climb up. Wash the pots. Build the fire. Swab the galley. Johnnie! Johnnie! Johnnie!"

But he never complained. He wanted to be a seaman. He wanted to be the best. The ship became his daily lesson book. Someday *he* would be giving the orders. "I want to know all about a ship and sailing so I'll be a good officer," Johnnie thought.

The men got so they would grin when they saw him flash by. He never seemed to walk. Soon they were wondering how they could have put up with the ship's boys they used to have before they got Johnnie.

Each night Johnnie reached his bunk bone-tired. But he would open his sea chest and peek at his precious brass spyglass to see that it was unharmed. Then he'd try to read a few lines in one of the books the Dominie had given him. But his eyes always glued themselves shut suddenly. And he never knew anything more until he was awakened in the morning by the cook.

"Shake a leg, lad," the cook would say. "It must be all the reading you do that makes you so sleepy in the morning. It can't be the work you do," and he would laugh in a joking way as Johnnie stumbled out of bed.

The collier worked her way from one town to another until she put into the big port of Kirkcudbright, down the coast from Arbigland. She dropped anchor in the bay among the many ships.

Johnnie leaned over the side. He held his spyglass to his eye and gazed in wonder at the vessels from faraway lands. Drawn up along the waterfront were lines of waiting carts which carried goods from ships to inland towns and villages. Boys were gathered in groups in front of shops or lounging on the sea wall.

"Want to go ashore?" asked the captain, walking up to Johnnie.

"Oh, yes, sir!" replied Johnnie.

"Then come along," the skipper invited. He started down the rope ladder to the skiff, which two of the crew held against the side of the ship.

"That's a grand spyglass you have there," the captain commented after they were seated in the skiff.

"It is that, sir," agreed Johnnie. "The laird gave it to me for my last birthday."

"Weel, take care you don't lose it, son," cautioned the captain kindly. "Kirkcudbright is a big place. Young ruffians sometimes make it hard for a new ship's boy."

"I'm not afraid, sir," Johnnie replied rather cockily.

The two sailors who were rowing brought the skiff to the steps in the sea wall. Johnnie jumped out and the captain followed. Pointing to an inn near the waterfront, the captain said, "You'll find me in there at four o'clock. Don't keep me waiting to go back to the ship."

"No, sir, I won't," Johnnie promised. "And thank you, sir."

[*63*]

He waited until the skipper was out of sight, then he swaggered up the street. He pretended not to notice the boys who stopped to stare at him. They laughed and called, "Hey, you lubber!" after him.

He swung his spyglass and paused to peer into the shop windows. He gaped at the ruins of an old castle. He made the tour of High Street and came again to the waterfront. He had been so interested in the streets and buildings, he had forgotten the gang of boys.

Now, it came to him quickly that he had been followed. He found he was in a rather deserted part of the town. And he was backed against a warehouse. Toward him from the left advanced three burly lads. On his right were four more, walking purposely in his direction.

He knew they wanted to pick a fight. Or they wanted something he had. His spyglass! He dropped it into the deep pocket of his waistcoat. He leaned over quietly and picked up a stone. Then he waited, his heart pounding in his chest.

He would not have much chance against seven boys. But if he could hold them off, maybe . . .

When the groups were a short distance away, they stopped. Johnnie tensed his muscles, ready to spring. A big towheaded boy stepped out from the right. He faced Johnnie.

"What you scairt of, little country laddie?" asked the towhead in a jeering tone. "We wouldn't hurt you. All we want to see is your spyglass. Give us a look."

He turned his head and winked broadly at his companions. They clapped hands over their mouths to hide their grins.

"You've not come to look through my spyglass," Johnnie told them calmly. "I think you've come to take it away from me."

At this all seven roared.

"My, my, bright as a button, aren't you?" said the towheaded bully. "Never saw a new ship's boy catch on so quick." He strode up to Johnnie and demanded, "Give it here!"

Johnnie brought up his arm and let fly with the stone. It grazed the boy's ear. He grasped Johnnie's wrist and gave it a sharp twist.

"None of that!" he cried, punching Johnnie in the face with his other fist.

Johnnie howled with rage. He tried to jerk his arm free. It seemed caught in a vise. The

He'd not let them get his spyglass, if he died for it!

big boy drew back to punch him again, but Johnnie lowered his head. He saw the boy's bare toes sticking out of the tattered boots. Johnnie stamped on them with all his might.

The bully dropped his arm and yelled with pain. Johnnie leaped forward. Several boys made a grab for his coat. He struggled and yanked. Cloth ripped as he pulled free. He ran blindly.

His legs churned as he raced along the shore. The boys, who were all bigger and longer-legged, gained on him. The spyglass felt as though it weighed as much as he did. He could not outrun the gang. The towhead, in spite of his bruised feet, was right behind him.

There was no fear in Johnnie. He was filled with anger. He'd not let them get his spyglass, if he died for it!

They were all running along the sea wall now. Johnnie's chest ached with every breath. He wouldn't be able to run much longer. He had to think of something!

It came to him quickly. Back home he and Rorie used to have a way of getting the better of the other boys. Maybe the same thing would work with these lads. He'd take a chance.

Suddenly he crouched down and sprang off the sea wall onto the sand.

The boys raced on for a few feet before they could stop themselves. Then they were after him in a pack, yelling in savage glee. They were having a grand time. No new boy had shown so much fight, or given them such a grand race, in a long time.

But it was just like the poor simpleton, they thought, to try the beach. As if it wasn't ten times harder to run in the deep sand!

But Johnnie was making straight for the water. He began wading out. His pursuers tumbled after him, almost bursting themselves laughing. They blew and puffed and gasped as the cold water struck their shins.

The water reached up to Johnnie's armpits. Diving down, he began to swim under water. His clothes and the spyglass dragged on him. Yet he managed to change direction and come up some distance away.

He turned and looked back. The boys were scattering for shore. They were shouting as they went, plunging and stumbling in a panic up the beach.

"Help! Help! Save him! He's drowned!"

they cried. He had vanished right before their very eyes. He must have drowned! Some of the boys began to whimper. They had only meant to bully the new ship's boy, not to cause him real harm.

Their crying and shouting alarmed some sailors in a rowboat out on the bay. They looked all about. But all they saw was a boy swimming with steady strokes toward the steps of the sea wall. And they paid no further attention.

"A daft lad off one of the foreign ships in the bay," they said. "If a Scots lad went swimming at all, it would not be in the dead of winter."

Johnnie reached the steps. As he stood up, he thought he would shake to pieces with cold. But he went up the steps, brushing past the cluster of amazed boys.

"Maybe you better learn how to swim," he flung over his shoulder, "before you start a fight with a new ship's boy."

Though he felt he would freeze before he came to the door of the inn, he was happy. Back home, he and Rorie used to get out of tight scrapes many times because they could swim and the other boys couldn't. He had

[69]

"The ruffians took after you, no doubt?"

taken the chance these boys wouldn't know how to swim either. And he had won!

He opened the inn door and walked inside. His captain saw him enter. He rose from his table and took his greatcoat from the back of the chair.

"Wrap yourself in this, Johnnie lad," he said, putting the coat about the boy and leading him to the fire. "The ruffians took after you, no doubt?"

"That they did, sir," admitted Johnnie through his chattering teeth. He warmed himself at the blaze for a moment. Then he took his spyglass from his pocket and shook it vigorously to empty it of water.

The captain gave his ship's boy an admiring glance. He said wryly, "I see they didn't get what they were after, for you still have your spyglass." He thought to himself, "No, and a pack of forty bullies couldn't take it away from you. You've the proud, brave, canny heart of a tiger, Johnnie, my joe."

CHAPTER SEVEN

He Becomes an Apprentice

FOR almost two years Johnnie worked as ship's boy in first one collier then another. But he did not want to stay any longer on the coal boats. He wanted a chance to better himself.

His parents and the laird were anxious too for him to think about his future. He was twelve going on thirteen. He had his heart set on being a seaman. They agreed that they would try to find a place for him as an apprentice.

On a spring day soon after he had left the coal boat and come home, Johnnie and his sister Janet were planting Indian corn in the cottage garden. He saw the laird hurrying down the path from the mansion house.

"Good morning," the laird said, opening the garden gate. "Johnnie, how would you like to be an apprentice to a merchant in Whitehaven?"

"What kind of merchant, sir?" Johnnie asked a bit doubtfully. Whitehaven sounded like more coal boats, for that city was a coal mining center.

Just then Johnnie's father and mother and his sisters Elizabeth and Mary Ann came out into the garden. They were surprised to see the laird at the cottage so early.

"The laird knows a man who has a place for Johnnie," Janet spoke up quickly.

"Ay?" said Mr. Paul, looking down at his son.

"A Mr. John Younger," the laird told them. "He's a merchant engaged in the American trade. Owns ships which sail between Whitehaven and the American colonies. He'll be willing to take Johnnie on as an apprentice."

Mr. Paul said thoughtfully, "Johnnie will learn something about trade as well as ships then. Apprentice to a merchant shipper is a good beginning for a lad."

"Whitehaven is only across the Solway," remarked Johnnie's mother. "Between voyages, he can come home to visit us."

[73]

"It's a good chance to be something more than a sailor," commented Elizabeth sharply.

"Johnnie, maybe you'll get to go to Virginia to see brother Will!" exclaimed Mary Ann.

The laird smiled. "Well, Johnnie?" he asked. "What do *you* say?"

Johnnie grinned happily. "It's exactly what I want to do," he answered.

Very soon after that, he packed his few belongings in his sea chest, said good-by once more to his family and friends. And he crossed the Solway to Whitehaven.

Landing in the busy port, he hoisted his sea chest upon his shoulder and walked down the street facing the harbor.

He had not far to walk before he saw the name, JOHN YOUNGER, over a doorway. As he stepped inside the building, a middle-aged clerk behind a high desk looked up.

"If you've a box to deliver, take it round to the warehouse at the back," he ordered Johnnie.

"I'm John Paul come to be an apprentice," Johnnie said. "I'd like to see Mr. Younger."

"Set your chest down and follow me then," the clerk told him. He ushered Johnnie into the office and left him with the cheerful-look-ing merchant.

"So you're young John Paul," Mr. Younger said. "You come highly recommended to me by the Laird of Arbigland, to say nothing of several others."

The merchant regarded him thoughtfully. "Mmmm . . . you'll do very well," Mr. Younger decided. Getting up, he went to the door. "Bring the indenture for John Paul," he called to a clerk.

The clerk came in at once and gave Johnnie a long hand-written form. The boy read slowly the terms of the indenture:

"I, John Paul, do promise to serve faithfully and truly John Younger for seven years. I will not go to taverns and alehouses or play at dice or unlawful games. I will not go anywhere without my master's permission. I will be an honest and diligent apprentice and behave my-self well at all times."

Johnnie took a deep breath. It was a long list of things he must promise Mr. Younger.

The merchant smiled. "Take heart, young man. The first part's the worst. The next part tells what you get in return. Read on."

Johnnie continued: "I, John Paul, will be taught the art and practice of trade and seamanship. I will be instructed in the best way and manner. And for seven years, Mr. John Younger will provide food, lodging, and all manner of needed clothing and washing for me."

Johnnie raised his head. "That seems fair enough, sir," he said, trying to sound very wise and grown-up. "If I may have the use of your goosequill, sir, I'll sign my name."

"Good lad!" the merchant said heartily and nodded at the jar of quills. Then going to the door, he asked two of his clerks in the counting-house to come in.

Under the eyes of the men, Johnnie felt very important as he signed the paper. They then added their names as witnesses and Mr. Younger signed his as master. Then he put the document away for safekeeping.

Turning to Johnnie, he said, "Come, we'll go out into the counting-house. You can work there until I have a berth for you on one of the ships."

Thus Johnnie began as a messenger boy. He sat on a high bench at one end of the counting-house, which was the company's main office. When anyone motioned to him, Johnnie ran to see what was wanted.

He learned to know every department of the firm. He knew the cost of all kinds of cargoes. Then for a while he was a shipping clerk. He spent most of his time on the wharves, watching the shipments the company sent to America. And he checked on goods sent to the company from across the ocean.

He became well known to the captains. And he could rattle off their names and the names of their ships without once making a mistake.

Shortly after his thirteenth birthday, Johnnie was called to Mr. Younger's office.

"I've a berth for you," Mr. Younger announced, as Johnnie entered the door. "You're to report to Captain Benson of the *Friendship*. You'll go on the voyage with him to Virginia."

CHAPTER EIGHT

Brother Will

THE *Friendship* was no ancient coal boat with threadbare sails. She was a full-rigged ship. From the morning Johnnie climbed to the crow's nest to see the last of the hills of home, he found new things to explore.

He went peering into passageways and down hatchways, like a kitten sniffing out a new home. He learned new things. Under the eye of a sailor, he even steered the great ship through the quiet summer sea.

Captain Benson took time to explain how a course was charted. How the different sails were used to catch the wind. The names of the ropes and lines and cables. And how the guns and cannon were used to protect the ship against pirates who tried to capture merchant vessels.

Johnnie was small and eager and quick. By the time the *Friendship* was half across the Atlantic Ocean, the men were calling him "Monkey" in a teasing, friendly way.

At night he lay in his bunk dreaming of the land ahead. And of visiting William in Fredericksburg. For Mr. Younger had said Johnnie could stay with his brother during the weeks the ship was unloading and taking on cargo.

One morning Johnnie awoke to find a sailor leaning over him. "Get up, Monkey, if you want to catch your first sight of America," he said.

Johnnie pulled on his breeches. He grabbed his spyglass and was out on deck in time to hear the lookout up in the rigging cry, "Land, ho!"

He rushed to the bow where a number of the crew were already gathered. The land before them rose in a green forest into the blue sky. The ship's course was changed and they cruised up a bay.

"You're seeing Chesapeake Bay for the first time," one of the men informed Johnnie.

The air was warm and lazy. It had an odor of damp earth and growing plants. Johnnie had never smelled its like before.

The ship entered the Rappahannock River. Johnnie watched the sides of the river. They passed boat landings, villages, and white houses nestling in the woods. There were flower gardens that ran clear down to the water.

This was America! Johnnie's heart went out to the beautiful land.

"You're seeing Chesapeake Bay for the first time."

At last they had reached the town near Fredericksburg for which the ship was bound. The ship was moored alongside one of the long wharfs.

"We'll go into the inn to see about the stage to Fredericksburg," Captain Benson told Johnnie.

"There'll be no stage to Fredericksburg until day after tomorrow," answered the innkeeper in reply to the captain's question. "Why don't you take one of the tobacco boats?"

Captain Benson found a tobacco planter returning to his plantation up the river. The planter would gladly take the boy along and let him off at Fredericksburg.

Johnnie shouldered his gear and went aboard the long boat with a single sail at one end. He settled himself in the stern with the planter.

The two rowers took up their long oars. The steersman stood on the plank at one side. At his command, "Row!" they sent the boat bounding up the Rappahannock River.

There were long stretches when the rowers made the boat fly over the water. Then there

[*83*]

were shallow places when they got out their poles and shoved the boat ahead. In deep water with a breeze blowing, they hoisted the sail.

As the sun was going down, they rowed up to the Fredericksburg wharf. Placing a foot in the clasped hands of one of the rowers, Johnnie was given a boost to the top of the wharf. His sea chest was placed beside him.

"Thank you for a very pleasant journey," Johnnie said.

"You're most welcome, young man. Now good-by and good luck," replied the planter, signaling for the boatmen to row away.

Taking his chest, Johnnie walked up the

wharf. A dock worker pointed out William Paul's house up the street.

Johnnie hastened toward the small half-brick, half-wood house. With thumping heart, he went up the steps. The door was open and he looked inside. A man and a dog appeared from a room at the end of the hall. The hound dog was barking and jumping about his legs.

"Down, Mopsey! Down!" the man ordered good-naturedly. He saw Johnnie and stood staring. Johnnie stared back. Suddenly he recognized Johnnie and came briskly toward him.

"Ah, Johnnie! Johnnie, my joe!" he cried. "I've been expecting you for a long time. Put your sea chest down. Come in. Come in." He held Johnnie by the shoulders and shook him fondly. Mopsey danced around, wagging his tail.

Johnnie smiled happily at his big, dark-haired brother. "I was afraid for a bit you didn't know me," he said.

"You're daft, lad. Even Mopsey recognizes you for a Paul," Will teased him.

Together they carried the sea chest upstairs to a bedroom. "This is yours, Johnnie," William told him.

Johnnie made a slow tour of the room. There were rugs on the floor. The big bed had a snow-white counterpane. The furniture gleamed.

He thought of his bed under the roof in the stone cottage at Arbigland. And of the hammocks and hard bunks of the ships. "This is my room?" he asked doubtfully.

"Indeed it is," answered Will. "My room is across the hall."

"Then I'm thinking I'll be living like a king," said Johnnie with a grin. A room of his own! He had never had such a thing before.

Will chuckled. "We're all kings in America," he remarked. "Now, let's go to see what my cook Louise has for your first meal at home in America. Afterwards I'll show you the tailor shop downstairs and the rest of the house. Laddie, you're going to be good company for your old bachelor brother!"

Johnnie followed his brother and Mopsey down the stairs. Supper—fish, roast ham and greens, hot corn bread, butter, jelly, cheese, and strawberry tarts—was a feast to him.

As Louise, in starched calico and white apron, brought a fresh pot of tea, Will said:

"If your last letter, Johnnie, had told me *when* to expect you, Louise would have prepared a grand banquet for you."

"I surely would, Master William," Louise said. Then nodding her black, curly head at Johnnie, she added, "And plenty of good food is what that boy needs. He looks like a picked bird. But we'll put some flesh on his bones."

Johnnie smiled. That was the happy beginning of a different sort of life for him. It was a lazy time at first until he became acquainted with the town. He spent the days wandering about, looking at the wharfs, the rows of buildings, the mansions on the hill, and the river traffic.

Nights he went to his room to read books on navigation, history, and biography. It was luxury to burn a light for as long as he pleased and not worry about the cost of candles.

Very soon Johnnie felt he ought to help his brother in some way. So when Will finished a new suit of clothes or repaired an old one, he gave it to Johnnie to deliver.

Will found Johnnie was good at mathematics and he let him make up bills for the customers and keep accounts.

Often Johnnie rode Will's saddle horse on some errand to a plantation. One time, when he was coming home after dark, he heard someone playing a fiddle. His curiosity was aroused, so he turned his horse off the road into the woods.

He saw a group of men around a campfire. Getting down off his horse, he crept near. A thin, shabby young man in front of the fire ended his tune and sat down cross-legged. Next to him was a red-haired lad, several years older than Johnnie. There were three other men in leather breeches and jackets.

Presently they began to talk about a young man who had lived near Fredericksburg named George Washington. Then they went on to talk of the new King of England—King George the Third. The fiddler had little use for the King and his taxes. In fact, these Virginians seemed not to like many things about the way the King was treating the American colonies.

The others listened, while the thin fiddler did most of the talking.

"Ay, and he has a bonnie tongue in his head," Johnnie thought as he listened too. But

[*88*]

it was getting late. He crept back to his horse and galloped home.

He told Will what he had seen.

"So you came upon Patrick Henry and Thomas Jefferson and their hunting party in the woods," Will said. "Patrick Henry keeps a country store. But he likes nothing better than to talk and to fiddle, and go off hunting with friends. The red-haired lad, Thomas Jefferson, is a great friend of his.

"It doesn't surprise me that they were discussing unfair treatment of Americans. There has been much grumbling against England since George III became king. All I say is, the King better take care or there will be trouble."

"Maybe they're right about King George," Johnnie said. "I've heard many people in Scotland say he would be a stupid ruler."

The end of the summer came and the *Friendship* was ready to sail back to England. So Johnnie returned to his life at sea. During the next few years he continued to serve as Mr. Younger's apprentice. Whenever the *Friendship* went to Virginia, Johnnie stayed with Will until the ship sailed back to England again.

Then one year he left Virginia and returned to Whitehaven to find Mr. Younger closing his trading house. His company had many debts and business was bad.

"I'm sorry, John," Mr. Younger said. "I wish you could finish your apprenticeship with me. But all I can do is return your indenture. You will be free then to do as you please. May you have all the luck in the world."

Johnnie took back the paper he had signed so proudly. "I'm sorry, sir, too," he replied, shaking hands with the merchant. "I hope things change for the better for you, sir."

Sadly and thoughtfully, he went outside to the Whitehaven docks.

CHAPTER NINE

School on a Ship

THAT night he sat on the Whitehaven docks, thinking about Mr. Younger. He remembered that the man had called him John —not Johnnie. Indeed, many people called him John now. That was a sign that he was growing up.

"I'll soon be a man," he told himself, "and I'm without a job. I must decide now what to do about it."

He looked out over the water. In front of him was a bright cluster of lights. They came from the men-of-war, ships of the British Navy, rocking gently in the harbor.

John's mind leaped back to the sea battles he and the lads at home used to have with their toy ships. An idea came to him.

He got up from the coil of rope and set out for the cottage where Captain Benson lived when he was not on a ship. He found the captain sitting, smoking his pipe, on a bench in his little garden.

"Glad to see you, lad. Sit down," invited Captain Benson.

"Captain, do you think I can get into the British Navy?" John asked eagerly as soon as he was seated.

"That's easy," replied Captain Benson with a chuckle. "All you have to do is enlist."

"But I want to be a midshipman, sir," John said.

"Want to get into officers' training, do you?" The captain sucked on his pipe a moment. "That's a different thing altogether. To be a midshipman, you have to be appointed by the Navy Office in the City of London. And the Navy Office won't appoint you unless someone important recommends you. Do you know anyone important?"

John thought a bit. "There's Mr. Craik," he answered. "He's important. He's the Laird of Arbigland."

"If the laird will recommend you," the captain said slowly, "I dare say you have a chance." Getting to his feet, he suggested, "Come, there's paper and quill inside. You can write to Mr. Craik. Send it off tonight. And count on me. I'll help you too."

After John sent his letter to the laird, there was nothing to do but wait. He could depend upon Mr. Craik writing to London at once. But to receive any reply at all from the Navy Office took time.

Then one morning Captain Benson sent word for him to go to Staple House, the gloomy office building on the city square.

"It must be about getting into the Navy," John thought. And his step and his heart were light as he entered the building. There was

Captain Benson waiting for him. Gripping John's arm, the captain steered him down the corridor toward one of the offices.

"They want to have a look at you, my lad," announced the captain excitedly. "Two gentlemen from the Navy Office and the commander of the Navy ship that came in yesterday are here. Go on in." He turned the doorknob and pushed John into the room.

Two men in rich satin suits and a third man in a Navy uniform stood behind a littered table. They seemed to fill the room and they made John feel terribly small and unimportant. He doffed his blue bonnet and tucked it under his arm.

Captain Benson entered the office and bowed. "Gentlemen," he said, "may I present John Paul."

John stepped up in front of the three and bowed deeply. The men looked him up and down, from his black hair to his neatly mended suit and worn black shoes.

"Do you know anything about seamanship and navigation?" snapped the commander.

"Yes, sir," replied John promptly. He no longer felt nervous. He clasped his hands be-

hind his back and stood up very straight. He
told how he had gone to work on colliers.
Then he told how he had been an apprentice
to Mr. John Younger and had sailed with Captain Benson to America.

He named a list of books he had read. And
he ended with, "I can spell. The Dominie in
Kirkbean taught me good grammar. And I
write a fair hand. Test me if you wish, sirs."

"Harumph!" One of the gentlemen cleared
his throat. He look down at a letter on the
table. He turned to the other men. "We have
this letter from Mr. Craik, the Laird of Arbigland," he said. "He recommends the boy
highly."

The three men put their heads together. They talked in low tones. They darted quick glances at John. They were deciding about him. John waited, trying to appear at ease, with his knees wobbling.

In a few minutes, the commander declared loudly and impatiently, "And I say he *will* do! You can take my word for it, he'll make a good midshipman. I don't care if his father is a gardener! I say accept him."

"Very well, very well," agreed the others hastily. "We accept him. He does seem an unusual boy."

The commander plucked a pen quill out of the litter on the table. He scribbled a note and handed it to John. "Here are your orders. Pack your gear and report aboard the Navy frigate at once," he said.

Outside in the corridor again with Captain Benson, John blew out his breath. "Whew!" He grasped the captain's hand and pumped it up and down. "I'm in the Navy!" he exclaimed. "I can never thank you enough, sir."

In less than an hour, John was ready to board the battleship with his sea bag over his shoulder. He called good-by to Captain Benson, who had come with him to the dock. He heard the captain's hearty answer, "Good luck, lad!" Then he stepped aboard the ship.

On the deck before him was a chunky young midshipman.

"Midshipman Stubbs, assisting the Officer of the Deck," declared the young fellow. "Which are you—a new ship's boy or a new midshipman? State your name in answering."

"John Paul, new midshipman, reporting for duty," John replied briskly. He showed his orders to Stubbs.

"Follow me," the other said.

John fell in step behind him. Stubbs led the way down the biggest deck and past the most cannon John had ever seen that close before. Dozens of sailors were busy scrubbing, polishing, painting.

John twisted his neck this way and that, trying to see everything. He was surely in luck to start his training on such a fine man-of-war.

Stubbs stopped before an open storeroom door. At his knock, a grinning old sailor appeared. "New midshipman here," Stubbs announced. "Needs everything."

The old sailor began to pass things out to

Stubbs, who tossed them to John. John soon looked like a street peddler. On his back was his sea bag, and a rolled-up blanket and a hammock. Clothes were piled on one arm. In his hand he held a tin plate, a knife, and spoon

"There you are!" said Stubbs. "Come on!" He darted away and vanished down a ladder.

John stuffed the clothes and tinware into his sea bag. And down, down, and down he went to the berth deck. There in the great open space the sailors' hammocks hung from the beams like rows of sausages.

"Swing yours over that cannon next to mine," ordered Stubbs, pointing it out. "When you've done that, change into uniform." Midshipman Stubbs leaned against a post and folded his arms.

John climbed on the cannon and hung his hammock on the hooks. He stowed his own clothes, books, and other articles in the hammock. He put on the uniform with a wonderful feeling of pride.

"You're not bad for a merchant sailor, Mr. Paul," commented Stubbs. "That's a bit of luck for you. The Old Sea Dog can't stand green midshipmen."

"Ummm . . . *Mr. Paul.*" John felt a warm glow at that. He asked casually, "And who's the Old Sea Dog, Mr. Stubbs?"

"The ship's schoolmaster, of course," replied Stubbs.

At that moment, John was startled by the cry, "All hands up anchor!" It was taken up by the mates on every deck until the timbers trembled.

"The commander has come back. He's

[*99*]

aboard." Stubbs sprang up the ladder. "Off she goes!" he shouted. "We're sailing."

John leaped up the ladder after him. He reached the bustle of the top deck. The ship's lieutenant shouted through his trumpet, "All hands make sail!"

John saw the men scurrying high up in the rigging and on the yards, spreading the sails.

They unfolded as if by magic. John marveled at how quickly it was done. The frigate began to move. It was grand to be Mr. Paul, midshipman, putting to sea in a warship.

Stubbs shook him. "The schoolmaster," he whispered fiercely.

John saw a medium-sized man with a back as straight as a ruler. He had a brown, wrinkled face and blue eyes, very clear and piercing. John quickly snapped to attention and saluted.

"Oho!" rumbled the schoolmaster. "We've a sharp one here, Mr. Stubbs, haven't we? Stubbs, muster the beginners' class. With a fair day, we'll hold class on the open deck."

Very soon, John was sitting on the deck with fourteen boys about his own age. Standing in front of them, the schoolmaster began class.

He put on the uniform with a wonderful feeling of pride

The boys had been studying about how the weather was forecast by the clouds in the sky. They recited the lesson badly. The schoolmaster thundered that they were blockheads.

"You never observe," he told them. "You can't tell sunrise from a signal flare. I wouldn't trust you to sail a wooden shoe across a mud puddle."

The boys squirmed. John hoped he would be overlooked the first day.

Just then he heard, "Mr. Paul!"

John leaped up, his heart thumping. "Yes, sir."

"How many guns has this frigate?" demanded the schoolmaster.

"I should judge about forty-two, sir," John answered at once.

"There's a real seaman!" exclaimed the schoolmaster, pointing at John dramatically. "You've been too busy getting squared away to count the cannon. Did someone tell you, Mr. Paul?"

"No, sir . . ." John hesitated. Then he went on, "I read that a frigate like this usually has forty-two or forty-four guns, sir. When I came aboard, I noticed . . ."

"Thank you, Mr. Paul," broke in the schoolmaster. "That's what counts—you *noticed* and quickly too." He bent over the class. He told them how quickly an officer must observe, must think and act. John listened to every word. At the end of his talk, the schoolmaster assigned lessons for the next day.

At the words, "Class dismissed," the boys scattered, quick as rabbits, all except John.

"Mr. Paul," said the schoolmaster, "I'm going to try you in the class for more advanced students. You'll have to work hard."

"I don't mind that, sir," John told him. Watching him stride away, John thought, "I like him. He'll not be sorry he put me in the other class. Not if I can help it, he won't."

The schoolmaster wasn't sorry. Neither was the lieutenant of the gun crew after John had worked with him for a while. Every duty John was given he did well. The ship's officers soon considered him an excellent midshipman.

John had proof that he was doing good work. Each week the midshipmen's honor roll was put up on the mizzenmast. For four months the name of John Paul was at the top of the list or very near the top.

His letters home were gay and full of the happenings aboard ship. He described the excitement of sham battles and night maneuvers. He wrote about Stubbs and the schoolmaster.

He was full of hope for the future. In one letter he wrote happily, "The reports on midshipmen were sent to the Navy Office in London last week. I was among those recommended for promotion. Tomorrow a list will be posted. I hope I'm on that list!"

That night John and Stubbs lay in their hammocks. They were whispering drowsily. Their hammocks swayed with the roll of the ship, putting them to sleep.

"John," Stubbs said suddenly, "you're counting hard on being promoted tomorrow, aren't you?"

"That I am, my laddie," John answered with a contented sigh. "After all, I've been on the honor roll right along."

"I wish you wouldn't count too much on that. You see . . ." Stubbs stopped. "Well, it's just that—well, other things count more than being on that honor roll!" he said fiercely.

"Oh, belay there!" ordered the sleepy voice

of one of the crew. "I say there, pipe down!"

"Pipe down yourself," Stubbs told him. "Listen, John, I'm telling you this for your own good. You're smart. But you don't know any more than a baby about some things. There are midshipmen who've been on the honor roll for a hundred years almost. And they never were promoted."

"I don't believe it," John declared. Stubbs was surely talking nonsense.

The first thing next morning, John rushed to the mizzenmast to see the promotion list. He read every name on it twice. John Paul was not on the list. There were names of boys who were still in the beginners' class. Boys who didn't know one sail from another. Stubbs was right. Other things counted more than making a good record.

He stood there, feeling numb all over. Then a hand dropped on his shoulder. He looked up. It was the schoolmaster.

"Disappointed, Mr. Paul?" he asked. John had never heard the Old Sea Dog's voice so gentle.

John looked away. His eyes were stinging and his throat was choked. In a moment, he met the schoolmaster's searching glance. "Yes, sir, I am. I thought I was doing well, sir."

"You are," declared the schoolmaster loudly. "Your name was recommended by the commander. But the promotions come from the Navy Office."

"I understand that, sir, but . . ." began John.

"Promotions are given to sons and relatives of lords and dukes and earls, Mr. Paul," the schoolmaster told him grimly. "But not to the son of a gardener. I didn't want to lose you, so I didn't tell you that before." He hesitated, then rushed on. "You see, I'm of the old British Navy. Boys like you counted for something in the old days. The commander feels the same way about good work and ability. But we can do nothing while the Navy Office in London is run by stupid men."

He walked away, shaking his head and muttering under his breath.

John felt lost. He didn't know what he was going to do. Then he began to boil with anger. He had earned a promotion. The schoolmaster had said so. The commander had said so.

Even Stubbs knew it! It wasn't fair. It wasn't fair at all!

He wasn't going to stay where he could never hope for anything better.

When the frigate put into Whitehaven the following week, Midshipman John Paul resigned from the British Navy.

CHAPTER TEN

Actor

IT WAS hot in Kingston in the West Indies, blazing hot. Gangs of dock hands sweated as they hoisted hogsheads of sugar and molasses from wharf to ship deck. In the market place, the women used palm leaves to keep the sun off the bananas, shrimp, coconuts, and oranges.

From his shady perch atop a barrel on a store veranda, John idly watched the scene.

When he left the Navy two years before, he had taken whatever jobs he could get. They were on merchant ships in the West Indies trade. John's experiences had been very unhappy. The ships carried slaves. John hated that. Finally he had decided that he would no longer work on such ships.

As soon as his ship had anchored at Kingston, he had quit his job as chief mate. And he had stayed on in Kingston.

Now he wanted to try a different way of earning his living. He wanted a change from seafaring.

Across the steaming street, John saw a man with a long roll of posters under his arm. The man stopped before a warehouse. Getting out his pastepot, he slapped his brush across the wall and stuck a poster up.

It showed a picture of a man in a curly wig. Below the picture, John read in big letters:

JOHN MOODY
of London
and his Company of Players
in Classical and Modern Plays
OPENING THIS WEEK!

John smiled. "Now, there's something different!" he thought. He left the veranda and stood in the white glare of the sun beside the bill poster.

"Mr. Moody wouldn't be taking on another actor, would he now?" he asked the man.

The man squinted at John. "Mr. Moody might," he answered. "No harm asking. You'll find him at the theatre."

[*109*]

John thanked him. The theatre was a few steps away on the main street. The front door was wide open because of the heat. He slipped inside. Up on the stage the actors were rehearsing a play. They looked as warm as the dock hands outside.

Of them all, Mr. John Moody appeared coolest. His curly wig was tied by a stiff black bow. His shirt was fairly fresh, though perspiration trickled down his neck.

"We'll skip to the duel," Mr. Moody was saying. "The rest of you may take a breather."

There were groans from two young actors.

The others promptly sprawled out on the floor.

John ran up the steps to the stage. "I beg your pardon, Mr. Moody," he said in a rush. "My name's John Paul and I've come to see if you have an opening for an actor."

Mr. Moody peered round at him. "I wonder how you got in? Well, no matter. What's your training and experience? Be brief."

"I'm a seaman, sir," replied John. "I've had good schooling. And I've educated myself by reading. I was in training as a midshipman in the Navy and . . ."

"Ha!" exclaimed Mr. Moody. "Navy, did you say? Go over there and wait, Mr. Paul." He motioned toward the side of the stage. "You may be a blessing in disguise." Facing the two actors again, he said, "Begin the duel. And remember, this is the most exciting part of the play."

Two young men stepped forward with wooden swords in their hands. They waved them in the air. The wood blades whacked against each other several times, clickety-clack.

It didn't seem much of a duel to John. He could scarcely keep from laughing at the way

[*111*]

He warded off their blows with quick, cutting strokes

the two young actors handled their swords.

Mr. Moody frowned. He glared at the two. "Gentlemen," he said in a withering tone, "you looked almost as fierce as two kittens slapping at each other." Turning, he beckoned John over to him. "Mr. Paul, in the Navy you were taught, I believe, how to fight with a sword."

"Ay, sir, with that and other weapons," answered John with a broad grin.

"Then show these actors of mine what you do in a sword fight," requested Mr. Moody politely.

"Yes, sir!" answered John. He selected a wooden sword from a pile of props on the floor. Going over to the actors, he said gaily, "I'll take you both on. Get a good grip on your swords." He waited, then cried, "On guard!"

The actors stood ready to fight.

"Now, my big braw lads!" shouted John. "See if you can touch me with those wood blades of yours."

The actors lunged at him. John danced aside. They darted after him, swinging their swords. John leaped back. He warded off their blows with quick, cutting strokes.

"Fight, men!" yelled John. "Be nimble or I'll nick your ears!"

Aroused, the actors went for John furiously. He ducked and struck aside their wild swings. The three men fought all over the stage. John egged on the two actors with cries of "After me, you cowardly lubbers! Faster, you snails!"

Swords sawed the air. Wood striking wood set up a clatter. The men panted and gasped. Their clothes were soaked with sweat.

It looked like a whale of a fight!

John leaped back of a bench. The two sprang toward him. One actor bumped his shinbone and stopped to rub his leg. The other jumped across the bench. John caught him in mid-air. The sword flew out of his hand as John gave it a quick, sharp upward cut.

"You haven't touched me yet!" John cried. "Come on, my bonnies!"

"Bravo! Bravo!" Mr. Moody exclaimed. "But enough, Mr. Paul. Enough for now. You can have another go at them tomorrow." He looked at John's sparkling eyes and wet, shiny face and announced heartily, "I'm going to hire you to coach the players. And we'll show the audience a duel they won't forget soon."

The actor who had barked his shin let out a loud groan. "Let him have my part, Mr. Moody," he begged. "I'll never be able to fight another duel in this heat."

At that all the actors burst out laughing.

"You see, Mr. Paul," remarked Mr. Moody with a smile, "you've fought your way into my company. And we welcome you."

In the months that followed, John became an actor. He was given different parts to play. And Mr. Moody coached him in acting during the company's travels. For the players toured the different towns on one island. Then they went on to another island, then to still another.

John was happy among the players. To make believe he was a king or a general or a knight was fun. It was all very carefree and different.

Then gradually he began to be less happy. He felt restless.

One morning after Mr. Moody's company had returned to Kingston, John woke up very early. He couldn't sleep. He left the inn and walked out on the wharf. A heavy mist was drifting in from the sea. John took deep

[*115*]

breaths. It was deliciously cool. If it would only rain! And if only there were high gray rocks along the shore with the waves dashing against them!

All of a sudden, it came to John what was wrong with him. He turned and ran back to the inn. He knocked on Mr. Moody's door. He must tell Mr. Moody at once. He gave several more loud thumps.

"Knock, knock, knock. Who's there in the name of Beelzebub?" demanded Mr. Moody in his grandest stage tones.

"It's John Paul," John answered.

"Come in before you alarm the house with your knocking," Mr. Moody told him.

John went inside. Mr. Moody sat up in bed and scowled fiercely at him from beneath his white nightcap. "What's the matter?" he asked.

"I'm homesick. Terribly homesick, Mr. Moody," John replied meekly. "I want to go home to Scotland."

Mr. Moody's scowl vanished. "I hate to have you leave the company, John," he said. "We'll all miss you."

"And I'll miss you and the others, sir," John

told him gravely. "I've enjoyed being with the company."

"Wait awhile," suggested Mr. Moody. "Perhaps you'll get over your homesickness."

John shook his head. "I can't wait, sir. I'm going out now to see if there is a ship sailing." And off he went.

John was lucky. He found a ship bound for Kirkcudbright, Scotland. He said a sad goodby to Mr. Moody and his players. He bought his passage and went aboard.

From the deck, as the ship sailed out of the harbor, John looked back at Kingston. Although he had been happy there, he was not sorry to leave. He faced about to watch the bow of the ship cutting a path through the water.

"I'm going home," he thought joyfully. "Going home to Scotland."

CHAPTER ELEVEN

John Paul Changes His Name

IT WAS June, a week or so after John Paul had come home to Scotland. John and his sister Janet stood in the doorway at Jamie's, the stonecutter. He was lettering a tombstone with mallet and chisel.

"I can't finish your father's headstone before you leave, Johnnie," said Jamie, tapping away.

"I would have ordered it earlier," John told him. "But I was in the West Indies when Father died."

"Aye," said Jamie and paused. "Johnnie, tell me, how is it you're a ship's captain?"

Before John could answer, Janet spoke up. "Both the captain and the mate died of fever on the way home. Nobody knew how to sail the ship but Johnnie. When he brought the ship safely to Kirkcudbright, the owners made him captain," she explained.

They heard hoofs clopping. Mr. Craik, the laird, rode up on his roan. He was leading another horse.

"Good afternoon to you," he greeted them all, stopping in the road. "I've been to the blacksmith's. Johnnie, if you and Janet want to ride home double, hop up on the other horse. No use walking when you can ride."

John got up on the horse and pulled Janet up behind him. "Good-by, Jamie," he said.

"Happy voyage, Captain Johnnie Paul!" returned Jamie.

John and Janet and the laird trotted out of Kirkbean Village toward Arbigland.

"Tomorrow," said the laird, "you'll be giving orders to the crew to set sail. How does it feel to be twenty-one and captain of a ship?"

"I feel as proud and happy as the time you gave me the old spyglass, sir," John replied warmly. "I was planning to go to sea then and to be the best cabin boy on a coal boat." He smiled and added, "Only now I'd like to be the best captain there is."

Young Captain Paul went aboard his ship

[*119*]

the next day. From then on, no one worked harder to be a good captain than he did. He made voyages from Scotland to the West Indies and to other places.

In a few years, he chartered a ship of his own called the *Betsy,* and became a merchant. He bought goods in London to sell in the West Indies. When he had sold these goods, he used the money he had made to buy sugar, rum, molasses, coffee, cocoa, and other products to sell in London.

One spring he loaded the *Betsy* with shoes, stockings, iron pots, kettles, and bolts of linen, cotton and silk goods in London, and set sail for the West Indies. On a sultry morning, he arrived at a West Indian island called Tobago and anchored the *Betsy* in the harbor of the town.

"All who want to go ashore may go," he told his crew. "I'll stay with the ship."

Most of the sailors started off at once in high spirits. A few hung back. They kept close to a huge sailor with shifty eyes and a red, puffy face. He was the ringleader of a group who were disliked and distrusted by the rest of the crew.

As Captain Paul turned toward his cabin, the big sailor called, "Hey, there, Captain! Where's our wages?"

John Paul turned back. "I'll pay you as soon as I sell the cargo," he said in a friendly tone. "I'm sorry I can't do it now. But I told you that before you joined the crew."

The sailor swaggered up to John Paul. "Well, we want our money anyhow," he drawled nastily.

"Men, I'd pay you if I could," John Paul explained patiently. "But I've nothing yet to pay you with."

The big sailor spat deliberately. "You're not smart, Captain," he said flatly. "Just hand us over some of the silk goods. We know where to make a nice little profit on them. Don't we, mates?" He winked slyly at the others, who grinned knowingly.

John Paul's eyes blazed. "You want the silks to smuggle into Tobago, do you?"

"Now, Captain," whined the big sailor, "you hadn't ought to call it smuggling and you wouldn't have to know a thing about it. We'd wait till dark and—"

"Stop!" cried John Paul. "From the start,

[*121*]

you men have dodged work, cheated, and bullied the others. Ay, I'd like to be rid of the likes of you. But you tarry breeks will get nothing from me to sell to dealers in smuggled goods!" He wheeled around and walked quickly to his cabin.

Through the open door he heard the sailors arguing among themselves. He thought they would probably get tired after a while and go ashore. He sat down at his desk. Before he visited the merchants in Tobago, he must check the prices on his merchandise.

For a time he worked busily. Then he noticed a perfect storm of yelling was going on outside. He heard his name howled with rage.

The ship gave a lurch and began to drift to starboard.

"They're taking over the ship!" he thought. "It's mutiny, by the great salt sea!" He jumped up. Grabbing his sword, he dashed outside.

Suddenly, out of nowhere, the big sailor appeared before him. With an ugly roar, he rushed at John Paul, waving a wooden club. John Paul stepped back. His heel touched the edge of an open hatchway. If he moved back-

He rushed at John Paul, waving a wooden club

ward he would tumble through it. He raised his sword before him to defend himself.

Lifting his club to strike, the sailor lunged forward. He missed John Paul and ran full force upon the sword. With a cry, he fell dead upon the deck.

For a moment John Paul was almost too horrified to think. He looked at the sailors, who were staring at him stupidly. "Drop the anchor," he commanded quietly.

At once the men obeyed the order.

"Lower the skiff," John Paul told the sailors. "I'm going ashore to report this to Judge Simpson."

He climbed down the ladder into the skiff. From the deck above loud voices were raised. "He's going to tell the judge, is he?" cried a sailor roughly. "We'll tell everybody in Tobago how he killed our friend in cold blood."

John Paul pulled quickly away from the ship. As soon as he reached shore, he hurried to the home of Judge James Simpson. The judge had known John Paul a long time. He listened carefully to the story of the mutiny on the *Betsy*. He shook his gray head sadly when John Paul had finished.

"Those men will raise a mob," he said. "Your life is in danger, John. If you stay on this island you'll be lying in a lane with a knife in your ribs before nightfall."

"The rest of my crew know I wouldn't . . ." began John Paul.

"They didn't *see* what happened," interrupted the judge. "No. You must leave Tobago at once."

"Is that the only thing I can do?" John Paul asked in despair.

"It is," replied the judge sternly. "It will be better for everyone if you go."

"But I've no money!" exclaimed John Paul. "There's my ship and the crew's wages must be paid and—"

"Our good friend Ferguson will take care of your ship and the merchandise and the crew's wages," said Judge Simpson. "He'll lend you money and a horse. Come."

He rose from his high-backed chair. Taking John Paul by the arm, he led him from the office to the back of the house. "That path through the orange grove leads to Ferguson's back door," he told John Paul. "Now, hurry!"

John Paul walked swiftly along the winding

[*125*]

path. The old Scottish merchant, Ferguson, was reading his newspaper under a tree in the yard. John Paul poured out his story. Almost before he had finished, Ferguson had called a stableboy to saddle a horse. Then he went into the house and came back with a leather purse.

"Here's fifty pounds," he said. "That will take care of your needs for a while."

The boy brought the horse and John Paul mounted. "Thank you, Mr. Ferguson. I know you'll look after everything for me," he said gratefully. "And keep fifty pounds for yourself after you've sold the cargo."

"Don't worry, I will," Mr. Ferguson assured him. "But watch out for yourself. Bad news spreads like wildfire. Those men will call you a murderer and people will be on the lookout for you, Captain Paul. Don't let anyone know who you are."

With a wave of his arm, John Paul was off. He sped through the narrow lanes of the town. He galloped down a road. He passed cane fields and windmills on sugar plantations. He left the main road. Setting out across the island, he entered groves of coconut and palmetto trees. Monkeys chattered shrilly at him.

[*126*]

About four o'clock in the afternoon, he came to a fishing village. A sailboat was drawn up on the sandy beach. A fisherman was overhauling his lines and nets. John Paul dismounted. Leaving his horse to stand, he walked over to the fisherman.

"Good afternoon," he said, trying to sound as though nothing were wrong. "I wonder if you would sail me across to the next island?"

The man lifted a sun-browned face. He looked from John Paul to the sky, and sniffed the breeze. "An hour's sail there, and another hour to get back," he said. "I'll take you, Mr. . . ."

Quickly John Paul spoke the first name to enter his mind. "Mr. Jones," he replied. Then he added, "I have to arrange for this horse to be returned to Mr. Ferguson."

"If it's Mr. Ferguson in the town," said the fisherman, "I'll have my boy attend to it when he goes to market in the morning." He shouted to his son on the steps of a fishing shack, "Look after that horse until I get back."

He stepped forward in the boat. "I'm ready, Mr. Jones," he said. "Shove off, will you?"

John Paul pushed the boat into the water. He climbed onto the seat in the stern. He had never been more unhappy in his life.

What a horrible day he had had! His crew had mutinied. A man had been killed. He had lost his ship and his cargo, and he had been forced to flee from Tobago—all through no fault of his own.

"I must begin a new life somewhere," he thought. As he watched the fisherman head across the channel, he considered what he must do. "I'll go to America," he decided at last. "There I'll settle down on a little farm in one of the colonies and be plain Mr. Jones, American."

[128]

CHAPTER TWELVE

Mr. Jones, American

THE name Captain John Paul was not heard again. After leaving the West Indies, John was called John Paul Jones or, simply, Paul Jones.

Now, two years later, he was living in Edenton, North Carolina. Every evening he went to drink coffee in Hornblow's Tavern. He was usually joined by his good friend, Joseph Hewes, who was a member of Congress of the American colonies. At the tavern they heard and talked about the latest trouble between the Americans and the British.

One April evening in 1775, John Paul Jones stepped into Hornblow's earlier than usual. But already the tavern was nearly full of excited men, women, and children. They were talking loudly. One man could be heard above the others.

"The British make us sell them our crops at the lowest prices," he was saying. "But they charge us the highest prices for their goods. They grow richer. We grow poorer. And the taxes grow bigger. Now King George has added still another tax. What for? To pay the cost of keeping ten thousand British soldiers in America. Ten thousand soldiers to force us to obey unfair laws! We'll be no better than slaves!" He banged a mug down upon a table. "I say three cheers for the farmers of Lexington! Let there be war against the British!"

The tavern keeper was listening so intently to the men that he had not seen Jones come in. Now he caught sight of him and hurried over.

"There's great excitement tonight," remarked John Paul Jones.

"Yes, a report came this afternoon," said the tavern keeper. "There was fighting between Americans and some British soldiers up north at Lexington, Massachusetts. Everybody here is for going to war."

"Ay, we'll have to fight," declared Jones grimly. "Will you please tell Mr. Hewes when he comes in," he added, "that I'm at the writing table in the corner?"

"Certainly, Mr. Jones," replied the tavern keeper.

Jones sat down and began a letter. "Dear Mother and Sisters," he wrote. "When I came to America, I gave up my seafaring life, as you know. Brother Will had died, but I found a good home among dear friends. Now I'm going back to sea. I want to serve America, the land I have loved since I was thirteen. I have asked my friend, Mr. Hewes, to find a place for me in the new American Navy."

He finished, sealed and put the letter in the tavern mail pouch.

"Ah, there you are, Jones!" Hewes, small and frail, picked his way across the room. Drawing Jones aside, he began to speak quickly. "This battle in Massachusetts has aroused all the colonies. There's a meeting of Congress in Philadelphia. I'm leaving at once. War or not, plans for an army and a navy will be rushed through. Come to Philadelphia in a few weeks."

"I'll be there, Mr. Hewes," Jones replied heartily.

On an early summer day, Jones, with his baggage, boarded a little American coaster. It carried all sorts of provisions and household wares. Her grizzled old captain put in at every port along the coast.

Wherever he stopped, people clustered around him to exchange news. The nearer the little ship got to Philadelphia, the more Jones heard of the fighting farther north. And the more people there were streaming toward the city.

When he arrived at Philadelphia, Jones was not surprised to find the waterfront on the Delaware River a very lively place.

All the fine inns were full, but Jones found a tiny attic room in a small inn on a side street. It was hot as a muffin just out of an oven. But he took it.

A few minutes later, he was on his way to the State House to see Hewes. When he came to the State House Yard, he noticed people milling about. They kept glancing up at the windows of the Assembly Room.

"That's where Congress is meeting," a man told Jones.

"Don't know what's taking them such a time to decide what they want to do," said a farmer. "I'm ready to fight now!"

Before long there was a fast-spreading mur-mur in the crowd. "They're coming out. See, there come the Congressmen."

Jones rushed over to the entrance. He and Hewes saw each other at the same moment.

"I hoped you'd get here!" cried Hewes. "We're going to fight! Congress is organizing an army. George Washington, that young gentleman from Virginia, has been appointed commander in chief."

"What about the Navy?" Jones asked eagerly.

"Plans for that come next," replied Hewes. "You will be among the first considered for the new navy." He drew Jones' arm through his. "Come, there's a good inn near by. I've had nothing to eat since breakfast."

As they went down the street, they heard men and women shouting: "Fight for Ameri-can rights! Down with the British lobster-backs!"

In the following weeks, Jones strolled often beneath the trees of the State House Yard. Inside the House, Hewes worked with the naval committee on plans for the Navy.

One day Jones saw General George Washington ride out of the city. The general was going north to take command of the army which was encamped not far from Boston.

Fall came. And John Paul Jones heard of how hard General Washington was working to get his army ready to fight. The British were in Boston and everyone was waiting uneasily for a battle to begin.

Jones spent many hours on the waterfront, talking about the war with sailors on incoming ships, and hoping he would soon be given a ship of his own.

One windy day late in November, when he was on the wharf he saw Hewes, with his great-

[134]

coat whipping about his thin legs, come hurrying toward him.

"Good news!" Hewes cried.

"At last!" Jones exclaimed joyfully.

Hewes nodded, his face beaming. "You've been appointed first lieutenant of the *Alfred*. That's our new navy's flagship."

"Ah, you've brought the best news in the world!" cried Jones. "I thought I'd go daft with the waiting. When do I go aboard?"

"The fleet will be right out there in the Delaware River within a few days," replied Hewes. "And you can report for duty."

On December 3, a few days later, a line of five ships lay in the river in the morning sun. On board all of them, men were scurrying about the decks. And officers were snapping out orders.

Lieutenant Jones, on the deck of the flagship *Alfred,* swung his spyglass up. One after the other, he observed the vessels and their busy crews. Then walking to the rail, he leaned over.

"The fleet's about ready to sail," he called to the man in the skiff below. "You can spread the word in the city."

[*135*]

He observed the vessels and their busy crews

Grabbing his oars, the man pulled hard for the riverbank.

Jones gazed around at the little American fleet. Neat, small, trim vessels they were. He glanced swiftly to see that all was in order on the *Alfred*. Then walking aft, he took up his station.

"All hands on the quarter-deck! Parade formation!" he commanded.

The crew came running and lined up, facing the mast. They raised their right hands in salute as Jones hoisted the flag of the first American Navy to the top.

All up and down the river, people had gathered by now. Jones took an instant to scan them through a spyglass. He recognized Hewes and several Congressmen waving their hats in the air.

"Ay, this is a great day for all of us," thought Jones. The next instant white sails on the five ships billowed out. The fleet glided down the river between banks lined with cheering Americans.

CHAPTER THIRTEEN

An Important Meeting in France

A THICK winter fog lay over the French coast. The American sloop-of-war *Ranger* moved slowly toward the French city of Nantes. Because of the fog, the sloop was barely crawling up the channel.

Jones, captain of this newest navy ship, was not letting foul weather prevent his reaching Nantes. He stood on deck watching for the dark blurs of other craft. And he gave directions to Midshipman Benjamin Hill, the helmsman, for steering clear of them.

"Steer small, Mr. Hill. Steer small," he ordered. "Keep her steady now."

There were many vessels hove to in the channel, waiting for the fog to lift. Jones couldn't wait. He must see Benjamin Franklin in Paris at once.

Congress had sent Franklin, one of America's great leaders, to France to get help in fighting the Revolutionary War. Franklin had made many friends in France. They believed America should be free from Great Britain. And they had already sent guns, ammunition, and some soldiers to help in the war against the British.

Now Congress had sent Jones to France with the latest, most important news of the war. As soon as Franklin received the news, he would go to the King of France and . . .

"Look out!" came the sharp cry as the *Ranger* passed close to a French ship. "You can't sail in this weather!" shouted the French sailors.

That made young Hill of the *Ranger* chuckle. "They should have seen you on the *Alfred,* Captain Jones!" Hill said. "Two years ago when you piloted our fleet among the islands down in the West Indies! Shallow water, dangerous reefs, high wind, and British warships—yes, sir, that was *piloting!*"

He gave another chuckle. "Then we landed and took all that cannon and gunpowder right from under their noses."

[*139*]

"We surprised them," Jones reminded him. "If you can surprise the enemy, you can win almost every time." He swung his arms about to get warm.

"You must have surprised the British plenty of times, sir," Hill remarked gravely. "I heard how you captured eight British vessels and then destroyed eight more—all in a few weeks. And that ship you had, Captain, the *Providence,* wasn't a good sailer. Can't think what Congress meant by making you captain of such a poor ship when . . ."

"Na, na," Jones interrupted cheerfully. "I had to show Congress what I could do first. They promoted me from lieutenant of the *Alfred* to captain of the *Providence.* I showed them you can win in a fight even with a poor ship. So Congress sent me up to Portsmouth, New Hampshire, to help Mr. Langdon, the shipbuilder, get this fine, fast sloop ready for sea. No, indeed, Captain Jones has nothing to complain of except this nuisance of a fog."

"Begging your pardon, Captain, but thunder, sir!" Hill burst out. "I wish we didn't have to stop in France. I want to be fighting!"

"We'll have great need of that fighting

[*140*]

spirit, Mr. Hill," Jones told him quietly. "When I get back from seeing Mr. Franklin in Paris, the *Ranger* is going into action."

The *Ranger* crept slowly up the channel. Before long, dim yellow circles of light pierced the fog.

"We're coming into Nantes," Jones said. "Bring ship to anchor!" he commanded the boatswain.

The boatswain whistled on his pipe. "Look alive there now! Shorten sail! Let go the anchor!" he cried to the crew.

Soon the sloop lay among the other ships in the harbor.

Before going to bed that night, Jones gave his officers instructions for putting the *Ranger* in perfect condition while he was away. And at daylight the next morning he had Midshipman Hill take him ashore in the skiff. A stiff breeze was blowing the fog out to sea.

"You may have good weather after all, sir," Hill said. He brought the skiff up to the wharf and Jones stepped onto the ladder.

"Hope so," replied Jones, climbing up. "But fair or foul, I'll be back soon." Standing on the wharf, he returned the midshipman's salute. Then he hurried off to find the posting-house where he could get a coach for Paris.

As he was walking about, a French soldier noticed Jones' red waistcoat. The soldier stopped to take a good look at the blue coat and breeches. He recognized the naval uniform. His face lighted up.

"American!" he cried.

In an instant Jones was surrounded by friendly Frenchmen. He explained in halting French what he wanted.

"Come," they said. "The American has not a moment to spare if he's to catch the first mail for Paris." And they hustled Jones up several streets to a coach waiting in front of a gray stone building.

They saw him into the coach and sent him off with merry wishes for a happy journey.

The fast trotting horses soon left the city of Nantes behind. They traveled rapidly through the bleak, wintry countryside. By nightfall, Jones had been bumped and jolted until he welcomed the sight of a wayside inn.

There he had a tasty dinner. And he slept crowded in one room with the other travelers.

At daybreak he was on the road again. Then late the next afternoon, he passed through a beautiful wood and crossed a broad river. The coach entered a wide avenue lined with elm trees. Soon Jones saw before him the marvelous city of Paris with its church spires rising against the sky.

[*143*]

For the first time, he saw the great old man

Within an hour he had reached Passy, a suburb of Paris. And he was driven to the mansion where Franklin lived. He stepped out of the coach and ran lightly up the steps to the great carved door. With his heart thumping, he pulled the big knocker several times.

A servant opened the door.

"Captain Paul Jones to see Mr. Benjamin Franklin," Jones said.

Shutting the door, the servant led Jones to Franklin's study. He rapped and called out at the same time, "Mr. Franklin, it's Captain Paul Jones."

A deep voice invited, "Come."

Jones turned the knob and went inside. For the first time, he saw the great old man who had worked so hard for America. Benjamin Franklin was sitting at a desk. On his nose was a pair of square spectacles. A pair of very bright eyes peered over them at Jones.

"How do you do, Mr. Franklin?" Jones began breathlessly. "I've come in the sloop-of-war *Ranger* with wonderful news, sir!"

"Ah, sit down, Captain Jones," invited Franklin.

Jones perched on the edge of a broad arm-

[*145*]

chair. "Burgoyne, the British general, has surrendered to the Americans at Saratoga, New York. A quarter of all the King's soldiers in America have surrendered. Think of it, Mr. Franklin!" he exclaimed.

Franklin rubbed his chin, then gave a satisfied nod. "John Loring Austin arrived from America a few days ago with that news," he said. "But to have you come in an American warship to report the surrender will make all the difference in the world to the King of France."

He paused, then went on, "The King has been cautious about helping us. Our fight seemed hopeless. Now he'll see it isn't hopeless at all! Our army has won a great battle. And Captain Jones has brought an American warship to France and is ready to fight the British."

"Do you think he'll send the French Army and Navy to help us in the war?" Jones asked.

"I think he will," Franklin replied gravely. He looked with interest at the slender man beside him. "Captain Jones, Congress has written me that you are to have a free hand with the *Ranger*. What is your plan?" he asked.

Jones leaned forward and smacked his palms on the chair arms. "I'm going to make a raid on a British town, Mr. Franklin," he declared. "The British are going to wake up and find the war on their own doorstep. Not across thousands of miles of ocean somewhere."

He rose and went quickly to the door. "I'm going to Whitehaven. That's where the British get coal. They can't make guns, cannon, and other things without coal. I'm going after that supply, sir!"

"May you have all success, Captain," Franklin told him warmly.

"I'll let you know what happens, Mr. Franklin," Jones answered as he left.

CHAPTER FOURTEEN

Raid on Whitehaven

FROM the *Ranger,* Jones gazed at the snow-covered hills of England and Scotland.

"Keep her head pointed up the Solway," he ordered Midshipman Hill at the helm. And he began slowly pacing the quarter-deck.

Seeing the familiar hills, Jones remembered happy times with his family. He thought of old friends. How grand he had felt when he was a cabin boy, sailing the Solway!

His thoughts were broken off by the lookout's cry from the mast top: "Harbor ahead off the starboard bow!"

Jones stopped pacing. He felt his fingers tingle. "What do you see?" he asked.

"I spy ships—three hundred or more. Harbor's full. They're black enough for coal boats," the lookout reported excitedly.

"Whitehaven Harbor, crowded with colliers full of coal!" Jones exclaimed. "Ah, that's grand! Now what about the fort? Anything doing there?" he asked.

"Not a thing, sir," replied the lookout. "Doesn't show any life, sir."

"So I'd hoped," Jones said. He remembered that when he was a boy, the British had paid little attention to the fort.

Soon after dark the *Ranger* anchored near a cliff outside the harbor.

"I want all hands on the quarter-deck," Jones told the boatswain. "And tell my aide, Edward Meyer, to bring me a lantern."

"Aye, aye, sir," replied the boatswain.

Jones, with light, springy steps, strode back and forth. He went over in his mind his daring plan.

"Captain, sir, here is a lantern," announced a voice.

Jones stopped. He saw Edward Meyer's face in the light. His eyes were alert and unafraid.

"Meyer," said Jones, "go to the carpenter, get a bucket full of spikes and some hammers. Bring them to me." He reached out his hand. "Here, give me the lantern."

[*149*]

Meyer darted off to find the carpenter. Jones hung the lantern to light the quarter-deck.

Soon the crew came hurrying to the quarter-deck and stood before him. Jones knew most of them were afraid. Their faces were drawn and their bodies held as tight as fiddlestrings.

Jones began speaking in a calm, cool way. "Men," he said, "we're going to make a raid just before dawn on the shipping at White-haven. I'm leading the raid. I need about thirty men to go with me in two boats. I'm calling for volunteers."

The men shifted about. There was a murmur among them. Then a lieutenant named Wallingsford stepped forward.

"I'll go with you, sir," said Wallingsford.

"So will I," said Hill, standing beside the other man.

"And I, sir," said Edward Meyer, pushing to the front with his bucket of spikes and load of hammers.

"Me, too, sir," said another and another.

Soon Jones counted twenty-nine volunteers.

He warned them, "It's dangerous business. We're all alone in enemy country."

The men nodded. "We understand," they told him.

"Very well," Jones said. "Mr. Wallingsford! Mr. Hill! See that a lantern, flint and tinder, fat pine faggots, and torches are placed in each of the boats."

"Aye, aye, sir," they replied.

"Meyer," Jones told his aide, "stow the spikes and hammers in my boat."

There was a continuous bustling about on deck. At last Hill announced that the two boats had been fitted out.

"Then lower away!" Jones commanded.

[*151*]

The boats were lowered into the water and the men got into them. In the darkness, they rowed slowly toward the harbor.

It was almost daylight when they beached the boats at one end of town. Ships were crowded together all along the waterfront. But there was not a person in sight anywhere. On the hill above them was the fort with a guardhouse at one corner. There was not a guard to be seen! All about were British cannon with no one to aim or fire them.

Jones gave a low chuckle. "Well, my lads, just as I thought. The British are snug in their beds." Turning to the men in the other boat, he said, "Wallingsford, you and Hill go to the other side of the harbor." He pointed. "See those ships over there? Set fire to them. Look alive, now!"

He watched them start rowing across.

"Break out the spikes and hammers, Meyer," he ordered his aide. "Men, we're going to spike the cannon."

Armed with long spikes and hammers, the men fell upon the cannon. In a few minutes all the big guns were useless.

"Now for the fort!" cried Jones. "Keep

[*152*]

your heads down, men, and follow me."

Stooping over, the little group of Americans ran quickly up the slope to the fort wall. They crept toward the guardhouse. Then Jones, pistol in hand, darted for the open door. Turning swiftly, he put a finger to his lips and beckoned to several sailors.

They tiptoed into the guardhouse. There lay the two British guardsmen, asleep in their bunks. The Americans grinned. They glanced at the coil of rope on a peg. They went to work. Before the guardsmen could cry out, the Americans had them gagged and tied.

Then they spiked the cannon in the fort. As they started back to the beach, Jones cried, "Wait, men! Look across there at the harbor. I don't see any smoke! Do you?"

The men stared at the ships. "No, Captain," they answered. "Nothing's burning."

Jones felt his heart sink. "Something's gone wrong. There should be smoke from burning ships by now." He ran down the slope with his men at his heels. He saw Wallingsford, Hill, and their crew huddled around their boat.

"Captain Jones, we couldn't set fire to any ships!" Hill told him.

[*153*]

They tiptoed into the guardhouse

"One of our men deserted," Wallingsford explained. "Took the lantern and tinderbox and ran away! We had no fire."

"The deserter will alarm the whole town!" a sailor exclaimed in fear. "We'll all be captured. Left to die in British prisons!"

Jones glanced into his boat. The lantern had gone out! He walked over and stood among his frightened men. Midshipman Hill, who had been so anxious to fight, was trembling. Even those who had gone to the fort were afraid now. All of them except Meyer.

Jones said quietly to him, "See that watchhouse over there? Go fetch a light."

Meyer darted away.

"Now," said Jones, "I want six volunteers. The rest of you get into the boats, ready to pull away. Well, Mr. Hill, what is it?"

"I'll go with you, sir," Hill said. "I guess I'm all right now."

"Good!" Jones said. "Any more volunteers?"

"Me, sir," spoke up another.

Jones soon had six volunteers.

Meyer rushed up, his face as bright as the glowing faggot in his hand.

"The watchman thought I was an English seaman, Captain," he informed Jones gaily. "He thought I wanted a fire to boil some water for my morning tea."

"That's the lad," Jones praised him. "Those who are going with me, get your faggots burning. The rest of you, man the boats."

He lighted his piece of wood from the flame Meyer carried. He waited until the boats were offshore. Then he began wading out to a large coal ship. Meyer and the others trailed behind him. They clambered on board. They looked about, but saw no one.

"Gather all the dry stuff you can find," Jones said. "Make a heap of it."

The men scurried about the ship. Lumber, pieces of canvas, old rope, shavings, cotton waste—all were tossed on a pile. Then they pushed it down a hatchway into the hold where the coal was stored, and threw lighted faggots on top.

They found a barrel of tar and dumped that onto the fire. Black smoke clouds began to billow up.

Above the roar of the fire Jones heard the warning cries of the men waiting in the boats.

"Hurry, Captain!" they shouted. "The whole town's aroused!"

Jones looked toward the waterfront. He saw people by the thousands running in frantic haste along the shore.

"Let's go!" he called to Meyer and the others.

They scrambled down the sides of the collier and into the boats. The sailors rowed off with steady, rapid strokes. Jones saw men rushing toward the cannon on the beach and up the slope to the fort.

[157]

When minutes passed and there was no sound of guns, the men raised a delighted cry. "The British will never catch us now," they said.

"Well done, men," Jones praised the volunteers. He watched the smoke curling above the collier and saw the fire spreading to other ships near it. "Without killing or wounding a single person, we've taught the British a lesson. If British ships raid our towns, American ships will raid theirs. Now, pull for the *Ranger*. We must be across the Solway Firth before sundown."

CHAPTER FIFTEEN

The Bonhomme Richard

A YEAR later, Jones was again off the English coast. But this time, he was captain of the *Bonhomme Richard*. And he was leading a squadron of ships.

He had made many raids in the *Ranger*. He had captured many British ships. And he had been promoted to squadron commander.

In his cabin on the *Bonhomme Richard*, Jones heard his lookout call, "Sail, ho!" Before he could reach the deck, the call came again, "Another sail!"

"What sails are they?" Jones asked as soon as he was outside.

"The British merchant fleet, sir!" replied the lookout excitedly. "Forty merchant ships. They have two warships with them, the *Countess of Scarborough* and the *Serapis*."

Jones turned to the men and officers on deck. "We'll have our hands full this day, my lads!" He ran forward to the bow of the ship. Taking a spyglass from one of the officers, he climbed up the rigging. At the crosstrees, he put the glass to his eye. Far ahead, he saw the merchant ships fleeing in panic one after the other. But the two British frigates had hove to. They were waiting for the Americans. The great yellow *Serapis* bristled with guns.

Jones came down from the crosstrees and went to the quarter-deck. All hands stood at attention, waiting for orders.

"Men, we're going to have to fight one of the biggest warships the British have," he explained. "I don't need to tell you what the *Bonhomme Richard* is. She's just an old French merchant ship that we made over into a warship. But if every man will do his best, I think we have a chance. That's all, men."

He raised his voice and shouted, "All hands clear ship for action!"

A loud battle cry burst from the crew. Then the boatswain began to pipe and sing out the command, "All hands clear ship for action!"

The drummer boys beat the long roll. The

fifes whistled. Guns and cannon were made ready. Young powder-monkeys raced to provide gunpowder and shot for the cannon.

Jones sent some of the men aloft with muskets and hand grenades. "You can shoot down on the enemy's decks from the rigging," he said.

The decks hummed with preparation for battle.

Jones stood by the men at the helm. He inspected the sea around the ship with his spyglass and gave directions for steering.

The two British frigates, with flags and pennants flying, lay not far ahead in the twilight.

"They're waiting like patient jungle beasts to devour us," Jones thought. "Well, we'll see."

He began trying to gain a good position for the attack. Then in a few moments, darkness closed down on the sea like the lid on a box. For a while there were no sounds on the *Bonhomme Richard* but the creaking of wood and Jones' low commands.

Suddenly, out of the blackness, the great frigate *Serapis* loomed up close. Jones drew a deep breath and leaned over the rail of the quarter-deck. He spoke in a low tone to his first lieutenant, Mr. Dale. "Pass the word to begin the action," he said.

The lieutenant raced down the deck.

A moment later there was a terrible explosion beneath Jones. It rocked the *Bonhomme Richard*.

A sailor cried out hoarsely, "Captain Jones! Captain, sir! We fired the cannon and six of our biggest guns burst in pieces!"

Just then shots from the *Serapis* roared and crashed into the side of the ship. In sudden terror, some men on the *Bonhomme Richard* broke and ran for cover.

[*162*]

Jones' heart skipped a beat. For an instant, his throat felt frozen. Then surely and rapidly, he spoke. "Back to your stations!" he called. "Back to your stations, men!" His voice was not especially loud, but it carried to every part of the ship. It was fearless and confident. The frightened men returned to their posts.

Tackles were seized. Guns were run out again and fired. Jones took the wheel. He watched the *Serapis* circle his ship, making lunging advances. Each time, she raked the *Bonhomme Richard* with cannon fire. And each time, she got away before he could maneuver his slow ship to rake back.

[*163*]

"I must get alongside the *Serapis*," Jones decided.

All of a sudden, he was startled by a bright light. He looked up. The moon had just risen. Off in the distance, he saw two American squadron ships and the other British frigate.

And gliding past the *Bonhomme Richard*, so near he could toss a stone on her deck, was the *Serapis*.

"Now for it!" thought Jones. "Stand by!" he shouted to his men. Jones spun the wheel and the *Bonhomme Richard* swung about.

Her stern rammed into the forepart of the *Serapis*. Canvas ripped, lines broke, wood cracked as the sides of the two ships slammed together.

"Bring me a hawser!" Jones yelled.

The sailing master grabbed the end of a heavy rope from the wreckage on deck. He ran with it to Jones. Jones grasped the ropes dangling from the bow of the *Serapis*. He knotted them to the hawser. And he made fast the hawser to one of the masts of the *Bonhomme Richard*. The two ships were held securely side by side.

The *Serapis* let go with her guns. The *Bon-*

homme Richard swayed and trembled. Holes were blasted in her side. Water began to pour into the hold below. A breathless hush fell over the *Bonhomme Richard*.

Then in the silence, a call came from the *Serapis*. "Have you struck, sir?" shouted the British captain. "Do you surrender?"

Jones' answer rang out at once. "Sir, I have not yet begun to fight!" he cried.

The crew of the *Bonhomme Richard* let out a wild roar of approval. The gunners began to fire. The men perched in the tops raked the deck of the *Serapis* with musket balls and hand grenades.

Jones darted from one part of the ship to another. He was everywhere. He was below decks, helping the men at the pumps. He was with the group of sailors dragging bags of sand to put out fires.

He lifted a wounded man away from a cannon. And he took over the firing himself until another could take his place.

For all, Jones had a word of courage. Over and over again in quiet tones, he would say, "We'll win yet. Hold fast, my bonnies! Hold fast!"

"Sir, I have not yet begun to fight!" he cried

The men took heart. They knew they must win with Captain Jones fighting beside them.

Once again on the quarter-deck, Jones peered through dense clouds of smoke toward the *Serapis.*

"You aloft!" he called up to the men in the rigging. "Throw your grenades down the open hatchways of the *Serapis.* Down the hatchways!"

Instantly, Jones saw the grenades dropping. Then there was one explosion, then another. Flames leaped up. The grenades had set afire the stores of gunpowder in the hold of the *Serapis.*

A gunner on the *Bonhomme Richard* hit the mainmast of the *Serapis.* It toppled and fell. All firing from the *Serapis* stopped suddenly.

"Captain Jones! Captain Jones!"

Jones looked up at the sailor in the cross-trees. "What is it?" he asked.

"They're hauling down their colors, sir!" answered the sailor.

"Do you hear, my brave lads?" Jones shouted to those near him. "They've struck their colors! They've surrendered!"

CHAPTER SIXTEEN

Celebration at Portsmouth

AT JOHN LANGDON'S shipyard in Portsmouth, New Hampshire, the first 74-gun warship, the *America,* was being built for the American Navy.

Carpenters hammered the planks of the ship's sides and decks in place. The caulkers pounded strips of packing into the cracks between the planks. Boys with big brushes sealed the seams with hot tar. All day and all night, the rank odor of tar hung in the air.

"That's a good smell. It doesn't bother us a bit," said the people of Portsmouth. "Captain Jones will have that frigate ready for a sea fight before long."

Every morning when Captain Jones went to work, he thought grimly, "We must hurry and finish the ship."

He had been in Portsmouth five months. In June Congress had sent him to complete the ship and be its captain. It was now almost the end of October.

Every day Jones sat in the workmen's shack making changes and improvements in the plans for the ship. He wanted the frigate to be the fastest vessel afloat. He kept the hull neat and trim, so the *America* would cut through the water.

Above all, he insisted that the frigate be designed to carry a great crowd of sail. In gentle breeze or whipping gale, the *America* must be able to outsail all other ships.

One afternoon he pushed aside the drawing on which he was working. He reached across the table and picked up the model of the *America*. This was the way the real ship would look when she was finished.

"She'll be a fine frigate, Captain Jones," a voice remarked. "And the American Navy can well be proud of its first real warship."

The shack door closed upon a gust of frosty wind and a whirl of dry autumn leaves. Jones looked up to see John Langdon, the owner of the shipyard.

"Oh, good afternoon, Mr. Langdon," he said.

"Good afternoon, nothing!" exclaimed the shipyard owner. "It's suppertime. Come, now, put your papers away, Captain."

Jones had not noticed the growing darkness

or the silence outside. All work had ceased for the day. He smiled. "I didn't realize it was so late," he said, getting up.

Langdon took the ship's model from Jones and turned it about, examining it.

"Wait until the Navy and Congress see the real thing!" he said excitedly. "They're bound to see what a daring new idea for a fighting ship it is. When one of those clumsy enemy warships comes lumbering up to this frail-looking frigate—boom! All seventy-four guns on the *America* will let loose!" He laughed softly. "Why, the enemy will never know what happened!"

He set the model down gently and helped Jones tidy his worktable. Jones put on his coat and his three-cornered hat. And the two men went outside. They gazed up at the almost finished ship.

"It's a dream come true," Jones said happily.

"Not so fast, Captain," cautioned Langdon. "If the war should end tomorrow, who would need a battleship? In time of peace, it's merchant ships that are wanted."

"Nothing could make me happier than for General Washington to smash the British Army and end this war," said Jones. "But I will never stop work on the *America* until it is finished. And we must have many ships like her. Let me tell you, Mr. Langdon, it will be frigates like this that will win the next war. We must never forget that our country faces the world across a great sea. And to be a great country, she must first of all be a great power on the sea."

Langdon sighed. "Please God our country can win through," he said. "Now, Captain Jones, how about supper?"

The two men fell into step. "I expect you'll be back tonight to stand guard," Langdon said.

"Ay, that I will," replied Jones. "The British have threatened more than once to sneak in and burn my ship."

On the beach beyond the unfinished frigate, they saw the glare of the watch fire. But they could see no one on guard.

"Where are my watchmen?" cried Jones in quick fury. "By the weathercock of Dumfries, if they have left—"

From off in the darkness came the sound of men struggling and the whinny of a horse. A boyish voice yelled, "Let go of me, I tell you! Let go! I've got to see Captain Paul Jones!"

"Blamed British spy!" a second voice shouted. "I saw you trying to get at the ship to set a spark to it. By ginger, we caught ya!"

"No! No! You're plumb crazy!" cried the boy.

Jones ran in the direction of the voices. Langdon raced after him. Almost at once, they came upon four of the ship's watchmen. They were trying to pull a lad from the back of a horse. The young rider was putting up a good fight.

Jones shouted above the hubbub. "What's going on? You there, answer me!"

"Caught a spy," gasped one of the men.

"Came galloping fit to split leather through the woods," explained a second, angrily. "Singing 'Yankee Doodle,' he was, too. Thought we'd take him for an American soldier."

"No such thing!" screamed the boy. "I'm an express rider from Boston. I've got a dispatch for Captain Paul Jones."

"Ay, so you said before," Jones said. Reaching out, he grabbed the horse's bridle. He spoke soothingly to the tired, frightened animal. "Keep your seat, lad," he told the rider. "We'll take a squint at you in the light."

With that, Jones led the horse and rider over to the watch fire. The men made a halfcircle. Everyone stared at the boy and his mudspattered horse.

[*173*]

"If he's a British spy, I'll eat my hat," said Langdon. "Just look at him!"

The rider was a lanky boy of fifteen or sixteen. He was dressed in threadbare trousers, tattered linen jacket, and a cap stuck full of turkey feathers. His weary horse stood quietly now with head lowered.

"I'm Captain Paul Jones," Jones said. "Where's your dispatch?"

The boy slid from the saddle. Reaching beneath his jacket, he pulled out a folded and sealed paper. "Captain Jones, sir," he said, touching his cap in salute. "Dispatch from the Navy Yard at Boston." He touched his cap again and handed the paper to Jones.

Jones returned the salute. Breaking the seal, he held the paper to the firelight. He read the brief note. Then read it again. "The Lord be praised!" he said softly. "The British Army has surrendered to General Washington at Yorktown, Virginia."

The boy whooped with delight. "We've licked 'em! Oh, thunder and lightning! We've thumped them British good and plenty!"

The watchmen clapped each other on the back gleefully.

[*174*]

"We must get the news to everyone in town," Jones said briskly. "If the people will come to the ship, I'll make the announcement to all of them." He grasped the boy's arm and exclaimed, "Oh, laddie, you've brought us the grandest news in the world this night!"

"I live nearest," Langdon said. "I'll ride through the town and spread the news." He took the reins from the boy's hands. "You and your horse are coming home with me to get something to eat."

When they had gone, Jones turned to the watchmen. "We'll need to light up the place," he said.

"Captain Jones, we'll have it as bright as day in no time," they promised.

They brought lanterns from the storehouse in the shipyard. They lighted them and Jones strung them all around the deck of the ship. The men set bonfires going along the shore.

Soon all the church bells in Portsmouth began to peal. And people began to stream into the shipyard. Men, women, and children came shouting and running and singing. They gathered all around the ship in a joyful uproar.

Jones mounted a keg of nails on the deck

[*175*]

where all could see him. He looked down into the sea of upturned, eager faces. He lifted his arms for silence. The noise gradually died.

Then Jones spoke in his strong, clear voice.

"Americans," he said, "our army has just won the greatest victory in all these years of war. General Washington has informed me that on the 19th of October, 1781, five thousand British troops under General Cornwallis surrendered to him."

There was a burst of cheers and shrill whistles. "Hooray! Hooray!" people shouted. "We walloped 'em! We've won!"

Men tossed their hats in the air. "It's over! It's over! The war's over!" they cried.

"Wait! Wait, everybody!" It was old Chips, the ship's carpenter, yelling at the top of his lungs. He stood part way up a ladder that went up to the deck of the ship.

Just as suddenly as it had started, the shouting stopped. All became very still.

"If you don't mind, Captain," Chips said. "I've got something I want to say to everybody."

"Of course, Chips. Come on up," Jones invited.

[*176*]

There was a friendly murmuring in the crowd. Everyone knew Chips. Very lively, the old carpenter climbed up and swung onto the deck.

"Neighbors," he began, "remember back when Captain Jones sailed out of this harbor?"

"Sure do!" a man shouted.

"Good!" Chips said. "Didn't he take the *Ranger* out and lick the British on their own ground?"

"That's right!" a young sailor in the crowd declared.

"And didn't he win the greatest sea fight in history with that old tub, the *Bonhomme Richard?*" demanded Chips. "Don't people all over the world have respect for Americans now? Who's to thank for that, eh?"

"Jones!" rose the shout from all sides. "Captain Jones!"

"Well, then," cried Chips. "Three cheers for Captain John Paul Jones! Hip-hip!"

"Hurrah!" burst from a thousand throats.

"Hip-hip!"

"Hurrah!"

"Hip-hip!"

[*177*]

"HURRAH!"

Chips moved forward and leaned over the rail. The crowd fell silent.

"Now, hear this," he said earnestly. "Captain Jones would like to be off fighting another

sea battle right now." He paused. "But he ain't. Why? Because our Congress gave him a job to do. He has to finish building this ship I'm standing on. And more than that," Chips went on. "He's busy on plans so someday we'll have the greatest navy in the world!"

[178]

The crowd roared lustily. Jones put an arm across Chips' shoulders. He bowed his thanks to all the people.

Then swinging around, he hurried across the deck to the signal chest where the ship's flags and pennants were kept. He lifted one out.

"Help me, Chips," he called. "We'll hoist the Stars and Stripes."

Captain Jones and the old carpenter tied the flag to a piece of timber high above the deck. The people watched proudly and silently. For a moment the flag hung limp against the pole. Then the wind caught it and whipped it out. The Stars and Stripes shone in the light of the many lanterns.

Out of the hush soared the voice of Captain Jones, "There flies America's flag of freedom. May it wave over our land forever!"

About the Author

DOWN ON THE GULF COAST of Southwest Texas where Iris Vinton lived as a child, the ranches stretched all along the water. So the cowboys knew almost as much about the sea and ships as they did about horses and cattle. They used to sit around the campfire, telling wonderful tales about storms, wrecks, buccaneers, and sea fights. Iris Vinton listened to them and remembered them, as she and other children climbed about old ships wrecked on the beach. It is no wonder that she soon began to write about ships and sailors. Besides writing stories for boys and girls, she edits the publications of the Boys' Clubs of America.

About the Artist

EDWARD A. WILSON was born in Glasgow, Scotland. When he was seven years old, his parents came to the United States, and it was here that he grew up. He showed talent very early, and when he decided to become an artist, he went to the Chicago Art Institute to study. Later, in Wilmington, Delaware, he studied under Howard Pyle, one of the most famous illustrators of all time. Edward A. Wilson's own work soon became widely known, and he has since won many awards and medals. Many of his drawings now hang in the Metropolitan Museum of Art and in the New York Public Library. He lives in Truro, Massachusetts.

Born at Kirkbean, Kirkcudbright, Scotland, July 6, 1747

Makes his first trip to America as cabin boy of the Friendship, 176...

Becomes a midshipman in the British Navy, 1766

Made captain of the brigantine John, 1768

Dies in Paris, France, July 18, 1792

Supervises the building of the first 74-gun American battleship America, 1781